Evidence

The Case For NASA Ufos

"A deep, 6-year, scientific investigation into Unidentified Flying Object phenomenon broadcast live by NASA throughout the 1990s Space Shuttle Missions"

by: David Sereda

Published by Terra Entertainment
Terra Entertainment, Inc., 12335 Santa Monica Blvd., Suite 336
Los Angeles, CA 90025

First Published in the United States by Terra Entertainment, Inc. 2002

FIRST EDITION

Contents

Forward

In September of 1986, my wife Donna and I were in residence at our home in Chilmark, Massachusetts, on the island of Martha's Vineyard. On this particular occasion there were two houseguests staying with us overnight. At about 2:00 a.m. I arose and stepped outside our bedroom onto the terrace wall to relieve my bladder. The firmament was magnificent, and it was natural for me to look up and observe its beauty and vastness.

After a minute or so, this contemplation was interrupted by movement at the far right in my field of vision. At an altitude, which I estimated at around 100,000 feet (previous personal observations of the Concord making its turn towards Europe over the island at half that height substantiate my estimate), were two brightly glowing white dots traveling in tandem at high velocity. My immediate shouting awoke Donna who came out to join me. She, in turn, recognized the mysterious glow. After a minute or so, this contemplation was interrupted by movement at the far right in my field of vision. At an altitude, which I estimated at around 100,000 feet (previous personal observations of the Concord making its turn towards Europe over the island at half that height substantiate my estimate), were two brightly glowing white dots traveling in tandem at high velocity. My immediate shouting awoke Donna who came out to join me. She, in turn, recognized the mysterious glowing objects, and we both vocally aroused the couple who were asleep in the guest bedroom.

Drawn by the urgent and excited tenor of our voices, they too emerged and observed these two objects track across the night sky. It took less than a minute for the tiny, perfectly round, luminous bodies to traverse from right to left across the entire celestial array which was visible to us. The speed was evidently quite high.

We four agreed, through the filters of our pooled experience, that these could not be astral bodies, meteorites, planets, shooting stars, fighter jets, helicopters, airliners, or satellites. To me this was not some stirring revelation, for I have been intrigued since childhood by the possibility of such phenomena's existence. My sighting was a confirmation.

Like fifty percent of the North American populace (according to a Harris Upham poll), I have long believed in the reality of technically advanced craft with capabilities in speed and maneuverability far beyond any achieved by our aerospace manufacturers to date.

Roswell, Kecksburg, the last words of Captain Mantell, the account of Nebraska highway patrolman Herb Schirmer, the stories of Barney and Betty Hill, Travis Walton, Linda Cortile, and the Pascagoula and Alagash incidents are well known to me and to millions of people.

When this subject is discussed in my presence, people often say to me, "Dan, these are anecdotes! Where are the pictures, film, and videotape evidence?"

In fact, there are hundreds of thousands of such anecdotes (see the Laurence Rockefeller-funded report), thousands of hours of professional and home video (the Japanese Nippon TV footage of Area 51), and film dating from as early as the 1950s.

Dr. Roger Leir has made his life's work the extraction and analysis of implanted objects from people who share the abduction experiences which have been catalogued by Bud Hopkins and Dr. John Mack.

In my view and in that of millions like me, there is no question as to the existence in multiple of these advanced machines and in diverse forms-discs, crosses, wedges, triangles, boomerangs, cigars, and their respective occupants in various manifestations-greys, blues, humanoids, reptilians, and Mothmen, etc. The question is not whether they exist but rather are some of them here to do our species harm or good?

The book which you are about to read offers the most logical, precise, and well thought through postulation that is now available to the public as to the mechanical/aeronautical basis for one type of these machines' existence, how they travel here into our observable dimensions and also the purpose for their occupants' visitations to our planet.

As the goal of the UFO movement, since Roswell in 1947, has been to expose the government's knowledge of the UFO phenomena and the existence of extraterrestrial intelligence, this may be the most shocking and powerful case presented at the dawn of the age of the New Millennium to expose the hidden secrecy. This postulation is not based on the anecdotes, film, video, and data previously assembled, but rather on the United States government's own N.A.S.A. footage photographed by astronauts on numerous space shuttle missions, broadcast live to Earth during the 1990s. It is also based on deep, investigational, written correspondence between the author of this book and some of NASA's top research scientists. Finally, it provides empirical, ancient archaeological evidence.

After reading this book, you will conclude as I did that the quality and volume of the evidence is irrefutable and undeniable. Further, it prepares us for perhaps the most vital revelation which will be unveiled to us in the new millennium-that we are far from alone in the multiverse and that there is at least one species of extra-dimensional/terrestrial entity which is very interested in our own well being and survival in a most profound and wonderfully positive way.

Dan Aykroyd
C.M., D. Lit. (H.C.)

Introduction

In 1968, when I was 7 years old, I was on my way home from elementary school in Berkeley, California with my friend Tommy. In those days, I watched the TV show "Star Trek" with my three brothers after school. I knew what a spaceship was. Tommy and I noticed a large crowd of people pointing up into the clear blue California sky. We stood in the center of the street and looked up to see a large, circular spaceship hovering about 3,000 feet above the city. It was metallic-silver in color, shaped like the "Star Trek Enterprise" except it didn't have any structure outside of a perfect circle. The crowds were gathering. People were coming out of their houses to look. Even a city worker in a man-hole came out to see.

Tommy and I thought the spaceship we were seeing must have been an American ship. Where else could it have come from? The crowds watched this thing for over fifteen minutes, then the ship just blinked out. It didn't accelerate. It just went into another dimension in a blink of an eye. We couldn't believe our eyes. We were both only seven years old. We didn't know that the government of The United States of America's space program was just in its infancy. Inter-dimensional shifts were far beyond the reaches of NASA. We had no idea what the significance of what we had seen was.

For the rest of my life, I would remember that day like it happened yesterday. I recapitulated the incident hundreds of times in my mind. When I later learned that inter-dimensional craft hadn't been developed by NASA, and that UFO sightings marveled the world since the Roswell Incident in July, 1947, I knew that what Tommy and I had seen that day was a "close encounter" with an extraterrestrial spaceship. No one could tell me what I saw was a frisbee, a pizza, or a hallucination. I knew it was real. I didn't need Freudian psychoanalysts to tell me that a frisbee can't hover for over fifteen minutes, then move from one dimension to an invisible one in a blink of an eye. A pizza could never be as large as a spaceship and fly. A hallucination couldn't be happening to a crowd of over fifty people at the same time.

For weeks after the sighting, I kept dreaming about the UFO. In the dream, it would have one set of multi-colored lights that spun in a clockwise direction, while on the same axis, another set of multi-colored lights would spin in a counter-clockwise direction. What did this mean? I always thought it may be the answer to the craft's propulsion system.

I knew the dream was significant when I learned (in my mid thirties) that three physicists named John Bardeen, Leon Cooper, and J. Robert Schreiffer won the Nobel Prize in physics in 1972 for a discovery very similar to my dream about the UFO. This group's new theory in physics demonstrated that the interaction between the electrons and the lattice leads to the formation of bound pairs of electrons, which are often called "Cooper-Pairs." The different pairs are strongly coupled to each other which leads to a complex pattern in which a considerable fraction of the total number of conducting electrons are coupled together to form the superconducting state. Time forward electron pairs with a time reversed electron and the ultimate superconductivity state occurs where there is a "complete disappearance of electrical resistance." This was a photocopy of my dream. I thought this had to have some kind of significance. But that significance would take me over thirty years to figure out. The fuller meaning and significance to this finding will be dealt with in Chapter Six of this book.

For 53 years, since the Roswell Incident on July 5, 1947, the goal of the UFO movement has been to expose the government's knowledge of UFOs. While there were many alleged sightings, just like Tommy and I had witnessed, there was no clear evidence of the government's knowledge of UFOs. What was needed to provide the evidence would have to be Air Force, Military or NASA video footage of UFOs. Incident reports exposed by government employees were not sufficient without video or film footage.

In 1997, I would begin to co-form a partnership of three individuals who had the evidence that NASA had encountered UFOs on many of its 1990s space shuttle missions. This true story will show NASA video evidence, a scientific investigation at NASA and inside the UFO expert community, of what just may be the most astounding proof yet, that our planet is being visited by an extraterrestrial civilization.

Chapter One

Relearning How To Observe The UFO Phenomenon

"Recognize what is in your sight, and that which is hidden from you will become plain to you. For there is nothing hidden which will not become manifest." – Jesus said – The Gospel of Thomas

I – If Contact Had Already Begun, Would We Know How To Observe It?

What does it mean to observe? Are there phenomena happening right in front of our eyes that we miss each and every day? The great mystics of ancient and modern times have told us this just as Jesus told his disciples over 2000 years ago. Does to observe mean to keep our eyes focused on something, our ears focused on something, our sense of touch aware of something, our sense of smell aware of something, our sense of taste aware of something, our sense of emotion aware of feeling, or our sense of presence aware of something?

Have you ever caught yourself walking down an empty street and suddenly realized that your mind was so far away that you might have missed out on that which was plain in your sight? I know I have and I later realized how many wonderful experiences I have missed because I did not know how to observe. Learning how to observe is an art and requires training of the mind.

I spent my life training my mind and all of my senses. Still I can barely fathom on what it means to be aware of the vast spectrum of everything. I had practiced meditation daily for over 20 years. Why would I do this? Why would any person spend countless hours training their mind to become aware of what is plain in their sight yet hidden from a mind that is obscured by cloudy thoughts and random quivers of the mind? What is so mysterious about what is plain and in our sight?

I discovered that there "is" so much happening right under our noses, so much that we miss. Even in the simplest phenomena perceived with a razor sharp mind that is penetrating and mystified, the ordinary becomes delightful and filled with more of a sense of entertainment than the solar system of a Hollywood mind.

When I was a child growing up in the late sixties in San Francisco, we used to play "kick the can." Someone would kick the can and I would have to go find the can and count to five minutes and then go out and try to find everyone. My friends hid while I gazed up at a group of stars that shimmered like a gathering of diamonds. I much later learned that those stars were called the "Pleiades." I was so deeply mystified by them. Seven beautiful stars that were known as sisters. These sisters would be gathered together for a seeming eternity.

There would be two great mysteries in my life: the quest for the mystery of creation and another more complex phenomenon. One of those mysteries would make so much sense to me and remain a mystery yet the other would always make my hair stand on end and cause deep explosions of turmoil inside of my soul. Since I would never understand what should have been an easy mystery to solve, I gave up and partook of the mystery that would reveal itself to me, the search for the meaning of creation and perhaps even the very Creator who is still creating this magnificent universe.

Since the dawn of humankind, our eyes have peered into the heavens and asked many questions: Who and what created life on this pearl called Earth? What is the Universe? How far does it all go? Are we alone in the universe? If we encountered extraterrestrial civilizations, would they be anything like us? Would we even be able to communicate with them? How would we make contact?

If contact had already begun, would we all know how to observe it? We do know how to observe persons, places and things that are familiar to us. This we have learned how to do. Even so, there may be much about our observational skills that prevent us from seeing deeper into the souls of other human beings and the cosmos itself.

If intelligent life were to visit us from other star systems in our own galaxy, let alone from other galaxies, we know that they would have to have light speed (186,282 miles per second) or beyond light speed travel capabilities to have arrived at Earth in a reasonable amount of time.

I would assume beyond light speed but that would break the existing laws of physics. Considering that our nation's public space programs do not have propulsion systems and spacecraft capable of light speed, we would have to consider any visitors from outside the solar system to be capable of such speeds, therefore to be far beyond our current scientific developments.

If intelligent life from other worlds is advanced enough to travel at such speeds, can we assume that we could observe a craft travelling at light speed (or capable of light speed) or beyond using conventional observation tools? How do we observe space phenomena? We use cameras attached to telescopes that see light reflected off of solids, liquids and gases. The Hubble Space Telescope uses this same principle. Land-based cameras used to photograph still or motion pictures also use this same principle.

Considering Einstein's Law of Energy is equal to Mass times Velocity of Light Squared ($E = mc2$), scientists make many assumptions. The first relevant assumption is that no form of mass can reach the speed of light (186,282 miles per second) and remain as it is. That means no physical spacecraft can reach light speed and remain unaffected by the great forces of energy and mass.

Steven Hawking wrote of Einstein's equation, "A very important consequence of relativity is the relation between mass and energy. Einstein's postulate that the speed of light should appear the same to everyone implied that nothing could move faster than light. What happens is that as energy is used to accelerate a particle or spaceship, the object's mass increases, making it harder to accelerate any more. To accelerate the particle to the speed of light is impossible because it would take an infinite amount of energy."

Nikola Tesla had developed a more "Unified Field" theory in physics. While it was little known, it was published during Einstein's era. Tesla was the great electrical engineer who invented alternating current generators (trumping Thomas Edison in the battle of the currents), remote control, the wireless transmission of electricity, neon and florescent lighting, apparatus for the utilization of radiant energy, the carbon button lamp (now the electron microscope), the first safe electric, public streetcar, radio (U.S. Supreme Court ruled against Marconi on June 21, 1943), and over a hundred other U.S. patented inventions.

While Einstein was focused on light speed and saw all matter incapable of reaching light speed, Tesla was focused on gravity as a great force of energy in the universe. Published in a book "Lightning in His Hand" by Inez Hunt and Wannata W. Drapper on Tesla's life, there is a remarkable story of how Tesla proved his "Unified Field" theory. He took several respected witnesses into a dark room where there were only a few wires and two metal looking plates. The men inspected the room at Tesla's request for trickery for what science and magic was about to take place. When Tesla conducted the experiment, the whole room was suddenly filled with light, but no one could find the source of the light. There were no light bulbs. How, then did Tesla get the room to glow as such?

It is written in this book that Tesla said, gravity is a source of energy that unifies all fields of energy in the universe. He said that he created a frequency of gravity that attracted radiant energy towards gravity. Light was, in effect just one particular frequency wave, slowing down towards lower frequencies of gravity.

Tesla believed that there were frequencies of radiant energy that were more energetic than light (that light speed is not the greatest energy or velocity) and became luminous as these high frequency energies slowed down in their vibration rates to the speed of light or visible light.

Tesla's suggested theory was in stark contrast to Einstein's theory that light was the greatest speed in the universe. When energy slowed down even more than visible light, Tesla believed it became electrical wavelengths of energy. The light that appeared in the room was the energy present everywhere in the universe slowing down towards the gradient frequencies of gravity. He believed that there was a way to utilize and capture this abundant and free source of radiant energy.

Looking at the models of galaxies, we can now see that the black hole in the center of a galaxy is a source of gravity so powerful it causes all light and mass to bend and collapse into it. This model proves Tesla's theory to be very plausible. Today, only ideas in quantum physics are beginning to understand that Tesla was probably correct. We will leave quantum physics for a later point in this book (Chapter Six), when it has a better chance of surviving the evidence, which will be presented here.

Tesla died on January 7, 1943 in New York. He had met Einstein a few times. Einstein even wrote Tesla a letter on Tesla's last birthday. He had his theories published a few times but because the world was hailing Einstein as such a great physicist, Tesla's ideas were ignored. He was, after all, just a great electrical engineer.

Integrating Both Einstein's and Tesla's theories, we cannot expect to see a proposed intelligent spacecraft in transit going light speed by conventional means. In other words, if a spacecraft were travelling at light speed, beyond or even near it, the spacecraft could not be observed as a solid object. At best, it would appear as a wave of light or gravity energy. Because there is a lot of light in our solar system radiating from our sun and stars, we have a lot of other light to try and differentiate between what is a natural light and what may be a spacecraft (now a wave of light or gravity) traveling beyond light speed or even near it. How could an observation tool make such a distinction between natural light from our sun, other light from stars and a possible UFO? The signal (possible UFO) to noise ratio (background light) would make such research painful and require excruciatingly detailed methods of observation.

II - Understanding Light and Light Speed

We measure everything we observe by our sight, sound, touch, feelings and extrasensory perception. Our eyesight is dependent on light and the speed at which light radiates and reflects off of all that we see. If a light was cast upon our world that was so bright, it cast a shadow of the sun, what would happen to everything we thought was real? Would it all disappear?

Einstein's "Theory of Relativity" used the speed of light (186,282 miles per second) to give relationship to events that we observe relative to time and space.

In the Book of John The Evangelist, John asked Jesus, "Master, is there any material universe?" Jesus answered, "no." John then asked, "Is there matter?" Jesus answered, "no." John asked, "Is there a material body?" I will not tell you what Jesus said to that one. You will have to observe for yourself. If Jesus lives in a light that would cast the shadow of our sun, for Jesus there is no observation of anything relative to light speed. But we observe everything seen with these eyes by the grace of light. Light shines from our sun and reflects off of the radiant blue of our atmosphere giving us the beauty of blue sky. The light shines off of our faces in the morning and we can see each other.

When the light is turned out, what mystery lies beyond darkness? Suddenly we can see the other stars in the universe. The Hubble Space telescope sees other galaxies. The idea of a mystical creator of the universe seems more awesome now than it ever did at any other time in history. The notion of a creator who made the Earth seems like one great being, but who made the universe?

For certain, in order to see the creator, we must first observe the creation. We do that with the grace of light. If we were to make contact with beings from other worlds, we would need the grace of observation by light. If we were to make contact with a being from Earth (and we live in it), we would need light in order to see that person. Once the sun rose and I saw the eyes of my beloved. Without that light I never would have saw her shimmering eyes, nor would I have seen the face of Venus and Jupiter.

First we have to understand what light "is" in an elementary way. Light is in fact radiant energy. There are different frequencies to this energy. All light that is visible to the human eye is only a small spectrum of the total energy field of what makes up the radiant energy that shines from our own sun.

If a prism were used to discriminate the radiated light from our sun into its component colors, the visible light, which our eyes can see, makes up the part of the spectrum ranging from red to orange to yellow to green to blue to violet light.

As light is energy, each color represents a frequency of energy as light. Red light is the least energetic of the colors of visible light. Below red light energy is infrared light energy. It is usually detected as heat. It is invisible to human eyes but visible to some reptiles. Lower in frequency than infrared light are radio waves of energy. This spectrum of light energy is invisible to human eyes also, but exists as energy.

What is Light ?

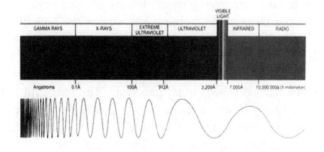

Light Energy Diagram

As light is energy, its frequency is measured in "angstroms." An angstrom is a unit of measurement for the length of a magnetic wave in the light spectrum. The longer a wave is, the less energy it represents and the shorter a wave is, the more energy it represents. The visible light spectrum starts at 7,000 angstroms at the color red and goes to 3,200 angstroms at the color violet. Ultraviolet light starts at 3,200 angstroms and goes to 100 angstroms. The shorter wavelengths of the ultraviolet are oscillating faster per second and are therefore vibrating at a higher frequency than the longer wavelengths of the visible light spectrum.

As light is energy, orange light is more energetic in frequency than red, yellow more energetic than orange, green more energetic than yellow, blue more energetic than green and violet light the most energetic of the visible light spectrum. Everything humans see with their eyes is within this spectrum of visible light only.

Above the visible light spectrum is ultraviolet light energy. It is light energy vibrating at a frequency with more energy than radio, infrared and visible light. Ultraviolet light energy is divided into three components: Near Ultraviolet the least energetic, Far Ultraviolet more energetic than Near and Extreme Ultraviolet light the most energetic. All three of these spectra of light energy are invisible to the human eye. Above these three levels of light energy are x-rays and gamma rays.

Now that we understand that light is energy with different spectrums, we can also understand that each of these spectrums represent different levels of actual energy.

Einstein's equation tells us that it also takes energy for any mass to have velocity. Just as we need energy to power a rocket, the energy frequency of our energy source can determine just how fast or how much velocity our rocket or spacecraft can travel. If a UFO was travelling at light speed or beyond, it would have to have an energy source that is well beyond our national space programs current publicly known scientific capabilities.

There are other problems with attaining such speeds with regards to passengers and safety of a craft. No solid object or spacecraft could physically or structurally survive the gravity forces of such high-speed turns as such a craft were maneuvering around asteroids and planets. If a solid craft were travelling at such speeds it would also be destroyed upon impacting with even a small object in space. At light speeds or even near it, avoiding collisions with meteors and debris in space would be impossible. An astronaut or passenger certainly could not survive such forces.

Even before light speed, the solid quality of a craft and its passengers would have to be able to transform into a wave of energy. As an energy wave, a spacecraft may not experience impacts or gravity forces any more. Modern scientists do not really know the answer to this problem yet.

It would take a phenomenal kind of propulsion system or other advanced transport system for any living being to travel from one part of this galaxy to another within a reasonable amount of time. Time becomes another interesting factor. It takes energy to create velocity in a solid object such as a spacecraft. The greater the energy frequency, the greater the velocity. The greater the velocity, the less time it takes to move from one point in space and time to another. This means that to conquer space and time effectively, we need higher frequency energy sources.

III – Space Propulsion and Light Speed

My observations about Earth were beginning to bother me in my early thirties. I thought everyone was going to want to build a future that was beautiful. I was wrong. There were only a few of us that wanted beauty. The rest wanted to keep on destroying the proverbial "Garden of Eden." While the masses were working as hard as they could to pollute this beautiful Earth, the only escape I could find would be to travel by starship to the nearest stars from Earth, Alpha Centauri 4.3 light years away. Because Albert Einstein didn't think light speed could be attained, other physicists and rocket scientists didn't either. We were bound by the laws we observed. They had to be broken to conquer the space-time continuum.

If we could create non-radioactive nuclear fusion, we would have a power source great enough to go to the stars and escape Earth's doom. This was my new plan. Build a spaceship and go to another planet that is more civilized and ask for asylum.

For an example, in the 1990s, I worked for a nuclear fusion scientist named Dr. Bogdan Maglich. I was trying to raise funding for and interest in his non-radioactive nuclear energy developments. I was interested in it because of the ecological crisis the planet was facing then and still is today. Most of the crisis was due to energy pollution: uranium mining, nuclear waste dumping, oil spills, oil mining pollution, emissions from power plants, trains planes and automobiles emissions from burning fossil fuels, etc. Maglich's non-radioactive deuterium-helium-3 fusion device had the answer to an abundant, clean energy source that could solve the world's problems. With over 5 Nobel prize winning supporters including Murray Gell-Mann, Glenn Seaborg

(Former head of the Atomic Energy Commission and Nobel Laureate for the co-discovery of plutonium), no investors in the world ever invested in the completion of his technology.

I was in the company of many of the world's leading nuclear physicists for nearly 10 years of my life. I always asked questions. The head of NASA at the time, James Fletcher, was a proponent of Maglich's work and asked the Regan administration for funding. He was turned down. I spoke with Dr. Earl Van Landingham, then NASA's head of Propulsion, Power and Energy about his interest in helping to realize Maglich's non-radioactive nuclear energy source for space travel and propulsion.

The fusion of deuterium (hydrogen) and helium-3 produces an enormous amount of non-radioactive nuclear energy: between 17 and 18 Million Electron Volts (MeV) per fusion. Dr. Van Landingham said to me, "18 MeV anti-protons could send spacecraft up to $1/10^{th}$ the speed of light (67,061,520 mph)," far beyond any speeds of modern rockets.

In comparison, the Apollo missions to the moon traveled some 240,000 miles in three days averaging a speed of 3,333 mph. Today's space shuttle maintains a speed just above 17,000 mph as it orbits around the Earth. If we were to actually fund this kind of fusion research, we might see benefits that propel us in future spacecraft to the stars at speeds of 67 million mph. Spacecraft traveling at this speed could travel from Earth to the sun (93 million miles) in 1.3 hours. It could travel from the Earth to the moon in 12.88 seconds.

Dr. Van Landingham also told me, "They are doing research into anti-proton space propulsion at the University of Wisconsin at Madison." The energy source is also compact, light-weight and ultimate for space travel: nine grams of helium-3 holds the energy equivalent to 1,000 barrels of crude oil.

This example shows how a very advanced nuclear reaction is capable of producing a much greater source of energy than rocket fuel, and therefore is capable of producing greater speeds for spacecraft.

You would think the technology would be funded immediately. It has remained in the closet since then. Private investors and governments refuse to get involved.

Considering that the nearest stars to our sun are over 4 light years away from Earth (V645 Centauri 4.2 light years, Alpha Centauri A 4.3 light years and Alpha Centauri B 4.3 light years), and upon a possible spacecraft from these nearest stars doing light speed, it would take them some 4.3 years of travel to reach us without stopping for gas and donuts. To reach us in one year, they would have to be traveling 4.3 times the speed of light. That takes a very high energy and high frequency energy source to accomplish. Sirius A and Sirius B stars are 8.6 light years from Earth.

Considering this basic understanding of light, energy, velocity and time, for any spacecraft to travel at speeds 4.3-8.6 times the speed of light, the physical structure of what the craft is made of would also have to be able to endure becoming energy vibrating at such a high frequency. Guess what, that also means the passenger would have to endure the same principle. That is because, according to Einstein, any mass object moving at any velocity becomes energized to a degree relative to its velocity. While Einstein does not believe in beyond light speed travel, Tesla's theories suggested it was possible.

Now imagine a passenger and spacecraft capable of vibrating with real energy near, at or beyond light speed. If they were vibrating with energy in the visible light spectrum, they would appear to have their own internal light (while in an energized state).

Tesla conducted many experiments where he ran a high frequency, high voltage electric current through his own body without electrocuting himself. After such experiments, he was witnessed to have a corona of light around his body. What Tesla was essentially doing was changing the vibratory rate of his body with high frequency electrical current. Perhaps he knew what I am philosophizing about here today. I am sure he knew more. Tesla also noted this phenomena in his lectures on high frequency experimentation.

If Tesla could induce a current through his body sufficient to cause his body to vibrate at a frequency above the visible light spectrum, he would most certainly appear to vanish from our sight. This would mean Tesla would be able to "see" into the invisible spectra of energy and light. This alone is a very advanced subject for deep investigation and experimentation, most of which is very little known to modern researchers.

If a UFO were to do the same to its physical structure, as it would be radiating energy as light above the visible light spectrum, we would not be able to see it by conventional observation tools and it would theoretically exist in another dimension that we do not understand. We would need a much more sophisticated observation tool to even observe the UFO.

The only way we could see a spacecraft or passenger that are capable of such speeds would be if they slowed down to a rate of speed and energy relative to the visible light spectrum. If they were standing right in front of us or hovering in a 3-mile wide spacecraft over our cities vibrating at an energy above the visible light spectrum, we could not see them with conventional observation tools. This would make such beings and craft inter-dimensional and invisible. In fact, science has already proven by this knowledge that invisible dimensions (other dimensions) do exist. We just cannot see them.

Could we have been visited by extraterrestrials already but remained unaware of how to observe them? Is NASA hiding evidence of encounters with alien craft from outside our world? Is the evidence right in front of us but we lack the knowledge of how to observe what is plain in our sight?

I would eventually find that NASA had learned how to observe into alternate levels of the light energy spectrum with super advanced cameras and that they discovered exactly what we had always hoped for: that we are not alone in the universe.

Chapter Two
The Alpha and The Omega

"To punish me for my contempt for authority, fate made me an authority myself" – Albert Einstein

I – The Government Covers Up Knowledge of UFOs

Government authorities tell the public that NASA has not found proof of extraterrestrial civilizations. They tell us this and we are supposed to believe them. If one does not believe in the empirical authority, one has to become an authority by knowledge and deep investigation.

Since the alleged crash of a flying saucer in Roswell, New Mexico on July 5, 1947, and a government cover-up of the incident, denying the UFO story calling the crashed saucer a weather balloon, the goal of the new worldwide UFO movement became to get the governments of the world to admit that Earth is being visited by extraterrestrial civilizations. For the past 53 years, the government and media position has remained insistent that there is no evidence that any world government has knowledge or proof of contact with an extraterrestrial civilization. Allegations of a government cover-up fueled UFO enthusiasts to expose the evidence.

At the Seti Institute in Mountainview, California, scientists use a vast array of radio telescopes searching the heavens for possible intelligent radio signals that may be being broadcast to earth. So far the effort claims nothing. Considering what we know about energy, and that radio waves are vibrating even lower than visible and infrared light, can we expect to observe a craft capable of light speeds and beyond in the radio spectrum of radiant energy? We now know the answer to that is probably "no." Radio waves are much too low in energy frequency to suggest an actual spacecraft being capable of accomplishing the task of conquering the vast distances of space in the time needed to travel from our nearest stars to Earth in 4.2 years or more. While radio waves represent the lower end of the electromagnetic spectrum of light energy, no one knows for certain weather or not they actually travel at the exact same speed as visible light and so on. Radio wave research at SETI claims to be looking for intelligent signals from spacecraft or planets that may inhabit intelligent life forms. Later in this research, we would learn that this is probably not where an advanced extraterrestrial civilization would be broadcasting information. It is much too slow.

We should be looking for an energy wave or particle (possible spacecraft) that is beyond or near the visible light spectrum. While this is the best place we can look for now, eventually we would have to assume that an advanced civilization would broadcast its signals far beyond light speed. But to observe beyond light speed, we would have to first conquer it. And this is just barely happening today. So, for now, we would have to observe in the upper spectra of light.

Theoretically, if we are to expect to observe a UFO capable of even light speed, let alone beyond it, we would need to see evidence of a gravity wave emanating from the UFO capable of bending light waves around it. Also, we would expect to see the UFO vibrating at a higher frequency of energy than regular solid matter. The answers to what I just presented would take time to reveal. These thoughts are vast and require a pre-arrangement of the mind in order to understand. That is what I am going to try and do in this investigation: create an understanding of complex ideas and make them simple. Then we can make real observations.

II – The Evidence Arrives

In 1997, I was contacted by a photographer friend of mine from Canada named Mike Boyle who had seen unprecedented NASA video footage of space shuttle missions revealing a possible UFO phenomenon. The NASA video footage was recorded by a cable TV station Program Manager named Martyn Stubbs during NASA's live broadcasts to the world. Very few persons anywhere on earth took the time to videotape all of NASA's missions beginning to end. Most of the missions were too boring to broadcast their entirety on any major

27

television network. In fact, it would be too expensive. But Martyn Stubbs did it. He had over 400 hours of NASA missions on Super VHS quality tape.

Mike Boyle described the events too me over the phone while I was living in Los Angeles, still trying to get funding for Dr. Bogdan Maglich's non-radioactive nuclear power. Mike knew that I had access to top scientists. He thought we should find this Martyn Stubbs and get him to give us a copy of his tape to introduce to the scientific community for a proper investigation. This was the start of my lifelong dream to explore outer and inner space.

Mike had seen a sample of the Stubbs video broadcast on a local cable TV station. He said to me that you could see these amazing objects flying above the Earth, in view of the space shuttle. Some of them were leaving the earth's atmosphere. For any object to leave the Earth's atmosphere would be impossible for any astrophysicist to comprehend unless it were a rocket or some object that has internal energy. It takes energy to escape earth's powerful gravity. Once any comet, meteor, shooting star or piece of space debris enters within a certain distance to Earth it falls towards Earth pulled in by its powerful gravity until it either burns up in the earth's atmosphere or impacts on the earth's surface or oceans. Nothing, not even a piece of dust can escape gravity. "So what could these objects be," if not UFOs we said to each other?

I asked Mike what the objects looked like on the video. He said, "Just round, fluffy kind of fuzzy balls of light." Neither Mike nor myself had a clue where all of this was going to end up and how much more amazing NASA video footage Martyn Stubbs had sequestered in his secret hideaway.

III – My Investigation of the Alleged UFOs at NASA Begins

I had read that a NASA scientist named Dr. Louis A. Frank had discovered similar looking objects (house-sized, fluffy and low density small comets) that were impacting the upper atmosphere. This was a brand new discovery in science it seemed. It was the subject of heated debates at NASA. The descriptions of Dr. Frank's objects were too similar to what Mike described on the tape so I thought they could be the same objects.

Based on mere descriptions, without having even seen the NASA videotape, I started thinking about who I could get to investigate the videotape while Mike tried to track down Martyn Stubbs. The most intelligent scientists at NASA, I thought, were astrochemists and astrophysicists. Astrochemists seemed like the first logical place to start. I went on NASA's website for the Goddard Space Flight Center in Greenbelt, Merryland. I found the e-mail address for NASA's head of Astrochemistry, Dr. Joseph Nuth, III. I was about to play a game of chess and "process of elimination" with him. I would go through every possible natural phenomenon in the known solar system with him and try to eliminate every one of them until we either came up with a plausible answer or the impossible word "UFO" was the only remaining alternative.

My first letter to Dr. Joseph Nuth, III, NASA Head of Astrochemistry is as follows:

Dear Dr. Nuth,

If these little meteors are hitting the earth's upper atmosphere and dissolving, wouldn't the intense solar radiation break the H2O into Oxygen and Hydrogen separated; thus releasing tremendous amounts of oxygen into the upper atmosphere? When oxygen undergoes further solar radiation, O2 (oxygen) transmutates into O3 (ozone). Could these space meteorites be healing our ozone layer? Is this proof that there is a God. Please answer.

I wasn't kidding about these objects possibly healing our ozone layer as a possible act of mercy from perhaps God or some higher intelligence. If one is keenly searching for the truth in any investigation, one has to be willing to remain unfixed about what the outcome will be. I didn't know if the possibility of UFOs would loose in this investigation on day one. I deducted that if these supposed, as they are correctly called by Dr. Louis A. Frank today, "small comets," were comets, they were made of dust, ice and water like all comets. The ice and water part does break down into oxygen, hydrogen gas and the oxygen does turn into ozone. More ozone would theoretically help our ozone depletion problem.

Dr. Joseph Nuth, III actually wrote me back. His answer was prompt. It is as follows:

Dear Mr. Sereda,

It has been known for a very long time that the Earth is under constant bombardment by extraterrestrial material (~20 kilotons/year) most of which is micron sized dust shed by comets and asteroids, as well as some finite number of larger meteors. The house-sized comet proposal is in addition to this known flux and is unique in that these bodies are supposed to consist mostly (or almost exclusively) of water. Because no satisfactory mechanism has been proposed to explain their survival in the interplanetary medium or their non-detection by a variety of other means (e.g. IRAS, COBE, IUE, etc.) most scientists do not believe that such bodies actually exist. The general belief is that the observations are valid, but the interpretation is wrong. Even if the interpretation is correct, however, the rate of deposition into the earth's atmosphere of oxygen or water is only a minute fraction of the amount that is already there, except in the uppermost layers (>100 km). For this reason, the additional oxygen would be much too small to measure.

If large masses of meteoric material (relative to the mass of the Earth's atmosphere) were to impact the Earth, the effects would be disastrous even if the impactors were only made of water.

Joe Nuth

What Dr. Joseph Nuth was doing with me would not be clear until the investigation evolved to a much deeper level. He was teaching me how to think like an astrophysicist at the same time revealing information that I would eventually be able to use in strong debates against NASA's top scientists to prove that Earth was encountering a terribly mysterious phenomenon that no one could answer. Ultimately

I hoped to get them to admit that fact, even if their admittance was inadvertent.

In this first letter, we learn that "The house-sized comet proposal is in addition to the known flux" of comets, meteors and shooting stars. That means that these objects in debate were new possible members of the solar system. He also admits that most scientists do not believe they exist just because they cannot explain their survival in the interplanetary medium of the solar system. This shows how stubborn scientists are: if they can't explain an observable phenomenon, they deduct it must be a false or flawed observation. So they test, and retest their observations until they either disprove it or eventually accept it. They will not accept it until they can explain it.

I started asking myself questions that I could not answer. How could any small body of water or ice survive the intense radiation from the sun while in transit from some other part of the solar system on its way to Earth for days let alone years without dissolving in a matter of seconds or minutes? Space is approximately –273 centigrade. It is freezing. But when any gas, liquid or solid object is exposed to the intense radiation in space from our sun and other stars intense heat is formed. There is no atmosphere in space to protect a small comet made of water and ice from the intense radiation from our sun. The question Dr. Nuth made was that "Because no satisfactory mechanism has been proposed to explain Dr. Louis Frank's proposed "small comets" survival in the interplanetary medium, he was concerned about this fact: Water and ice as small as these proposed comets should be could not survive radiation from the sun long enough to allow them to travel and exist in the solar system. Therefore the theory is flawed. What then could they be?

I wrote Dr. Nuth at NASA again the following letter:

To: Dr. Joseph Nuth, III,

Thanks for the info. So the phenomenon couldn't be from the comet. However, how would any object made mostly of H_2O (in liquid form) survive in space over any great distance unless it had some kind of phenomenal membrane to protect it? Wouldn't the H_2O, as you observed, absorb the intense radiation from the sun and produce heat, so much that it would dissolve into H and O? If the temperature of cold space is – 273 Centigrade, and upon exposure to direct solar radiation intense heat is formed, (at 1,800 degrees Fahrenheit hydrogen separates from oxygen), how would such an object travel in space for even a minute, let alone travel from one point in space to another unless?

Again, it takes time for an object to travel through space to get from its alpha point to its omega point. For a supposed small body of water or ice to travel through space would take time. In that time, the intense radiation from the sun would burn and dissolve a water body into its own transmutation and non-existence before it could arrive at Earth.

So how could balls of water the size of small houses be hitting Earth's upper atmosphere? In theory, it seems impossible. In fact, it may actually be impossible.

Dr. Joseph Nuth, III wrote me back the following answer almost immediately:

Mr. Sereda,

You have enumerated a few of the problems with Frank's hypothesis and probably now realize why few scientists think that the phenomena seen by Lou Frank are actually comets. No one doubts that he has observed SOMETHING, just not comets. In spite of the fact that many people are sure that Frank's explanation for his observations are incorrect, there has been no good alternative explanation proposed yet. I'm sure that there will eventually be one that even Frank can agree to.

Joe Nuth.

This letter was amazing evidence that NASA had discovered a new phenomenon that no one in the community of space science could agree on, yet no one denies that 'SOMETHING' has been observed. This 'SOMETHING' is unidentified and moves through space.

So far in this investigation, we have a NASA videotape revealing objects flying above our Earth that fit the same description of Dr. Louis A. Frank's observed "SOMETHING" but we don't know what they are. In the game of "process of elimination" we have eliminated shooting stars, meteors, large comets, asteroids and space debris. Space debris is the easiest to eliminate because most of it is too small. There is no space debris the size of small houses. We have not totally eliminated Frank's hypothesis that these objects are "small comets" entirely. Even so, we almost have. NASA's head of Astrochemistry is telling us that he does not believe that they could be comets because they could not have survived in space. We both deduced this fact.

What if we now suppose that these "small comets" are tailings from the recent passing of the comet Hale Bopp? Large comets are made mostly of ice and dust. When they near the sun they start to heat up and dissolve and flake off millions of water and ice particles. These particles refllect in the sunlight giving us the spectacular view of a comet's tail. Those particles, as the comet passes by Earth, could, in theory be where these small comets are coming from.

I decided to run this theory by Dr. Nuth at NASA and see what he thinks. Remember, if we are going to arrive at an answer, we must try everything known to science and either accept or eliminate everything. So let's try this:

To: Joseph Nuth, III,

Thanks for the e-mail in response to my question. I am amazed at how such a phenomenon can be observed, yet denial of its existence because it doesn't fit into the theory of the solar system. What are the chances that the H_2O house-sized objects are tailings from the recent passing of Hale Bopp comet? Any ideas? If you have any more thoughts on this, please send e-mail! Thanks!

This third letter to Dr. Nuth was about to teach us many things about science, NASA and how this community of minds responds to such an unidentified phenomenon. It would be the most revealing letter I had ever received from the American space agency or any member of a government agency, let alone one of its top scientists.

The letter from Dr. Nuth to me is as follows:

Dear Mr. Sereda,

I would agree with your amazement in the scientific community ignoring Frank's observations if it were true. However that is not the case. I know of no individual that does not believe that Frank saw something. The controversy centers on just what it was that yielded the signal. While he believes that house-sized comets of very low density are responsible for both the recent detection of water, and his previous (~1985) observations using the DE spacecraft's UV camera, few other people agree with him. [By the way, those previous observations would mean that the phenomenon would be a continuous process rather than one associated with a particular comet such as Hale-Bopp]. The reasons are many, but the best center on the fact that these objects should have been detected on several other satellites such as COBE, IRAS and ISO. These satellites have instruments that are very sensitive to radiation in the infrared region. These fluffy, house-sized objects should bee at a temperature near 300K or even higher as they near the earth since very fluffy objects are much better absorbers in the visible than the are emitters in the infrared. They should therefore be infrared beacons because they are so very close. Yet no other satellite has ever seen evidence for these objects. This includes a vast array of DoD satellites as far as I can learn.

Science is built on the premise that any hypothesis should have consequences that can be searched for or tested in some manner. If the subsequent tests do not agree with predictions, and the predictions can not be shown to be flawed, then the hypothesis is demonstrated to be wrong. This does not mean that we must have a better explanation for the phenomenon in question before we discard the flawed explanation. It simply means that we are still looking for a suitable explanation. Frank's comet hypothesis has not yielded any predictions that could be verified by observation that have been shown to be correct and has many observable consequences that are demonstrably false. Until he has a satisfactory answer for why we do not see what we should see in the infrared, most people will continue to believe that his interpretation of his own UV observations is flawed. They will however believe that he does observe something.

Joe Nuth

In the game of "process of elimination," we have just eliminated yet another hypothesis: that these objects may be tailings from the recent passing of the comet Hale-Bopp. Dr. Nuth answers this in the letter by saying "and his previous (~1985) observations using the DE spacecraft's UV camera, few other people agree with him. [By the way, those previous observations would mean that the phenomenon would be a continuous process rather than one associated with a particular comet such as Hale-Bopp]."

So we have yet another great mystery to tackle. This was a great possibility to suggest where the water was coming from. Now that we have eliminated this fact, the next clues as to how water can survive the intense radiation in space while in transit over great distances has to be merely hypothetical: There would have to be some kind of phenomenal membrane around the water body to protect it. That would have to make it a living thing.

The detection of water in liquid form is essential to indicate life. All living beings have water in them: microorganisms, plants, animals, mammals, humans, etc. The human body is made mostly of water.
Biologist Anders Hansson reflects that water, as an inert solvent, "is ideal for biochemical cycling." Szent-Gyorgyi (the Nobel Prize winning biochemist and discoverer of vitamin C) has called water "The matrix of life. Without it life cannot take hold nor could the evolution of life begin."

The human body and the pigment in its skin protects it from the amounts of solar UV radiation that Earth's atmosphere allows in. This is an example of a membrane protecting a life form that is mostly made of water. However, the human body could not survive the radiation from the sun and stars in space. It would burn up very quickly and die.

The kind of membrane these objects would have to have to protect them from extreme levels of cosmic radiation would have to be a phenomenon. Such a phenomenon would allow for a living entity or life form to exist in space. This is merely a hypothesis at this point. It would have to be proven by scientific means that are not attainable at the present time. This is because no one in the scientific community has gone public with the claim to have captured one of Dr. Lou Frank's proposed "small comets." So this next line of investigation or hypothesis would have to be scrapped for now.

The letter does acknowledge that the scientific community does agree that SOMETHING has been observed. It is now a greater mystery than ever. It gets even more impossible when you consider many of the facts presented in this letter. The most perplexing is the fact that these objects were only detected in the ultraviolet light spectrum and not detected in the visible light or infrared spectrum. Nuth describes this: "these objects should have been detected on several other satellites such as COBE, IRAS and ISO. These satellites have instruments that are very sensitive to radiation in the infrared region. These fluffy, house-sized objects should be at a temperature near 300k…They should therefore be infrared beacons." This is an impossibility to all aspects of modern astrophysics and chemistry. I will explain why.

The temperature of space in between stars is –273 degrees Centigrade. It is so cold that nothing could live in it unless it had its own energy. Planets and stars have their own energy. Planets have gravity, which is energy. Stars have energy from nuclear reactions taking place in them. But space is cold. If an infrared camera were to observe space, it would not sense anything in a pure void. But as soon as any gas, liquid or solid object moves through space, it absorbs radiation from the sun and stars. This radiation produces heat in varying temperature degrees depending on the chemistry of the objects. Nevertheless, any gas, liquid or solid in space produces heat, therefore should be detectable by infrared cameras or satellites such as Dr. Nuth has mentioned, "COBE, IRAS and ISO."

Dr. Lou Frank's observations of "SOMETHING" did not yield any infrared signal. These objects were detected using the "DE spacecraft's UV camera." Stars have a full spectrum of light and radiation from gamma rays, x-rays, UV rays, to visible light rays, to infrared and radio. But for an object to only be detectable in the UV range is unprecedented in science. This is why this mystery is even more baffling to genius minds. It may be this single fact that has caused scientists to call Dr. Frank's discovery 'SOMETHING" without going any further into the mystery.

We know from studying the model of light as energy that ultraviolet light energy is more energetic than even the visible light spectrum. We know that it takes energy to conquer distance through space in time. The greater the energy, the greater the distances through space could be accomplished in lesser amounts of time. Time and space travel are therefore relevant to the frequency and power of an energy source. If these objects are only visible in the UV range and not in any others, then they would have to be made of a mass of nuclear energy similar to what stars are made of: fusion. Stars are fusing helium and hydrogen. In the fusion of deuterium (heavy hydrogen) and helium-3, 17-18 Million electron volts of energy (MeV) are produced per fusion. Hydrogen is the "H" in water (H_2O). This great source of energy could allow for an object to have velocities that would allow it to travel at enormous speeds through the solar system as previously stated by NASA.

The problem with this theory is that it would have to answer where the oxygen came from to produce water. Hydrogen and oxygen would have to fuse to create water. Where would the oxygen come from? Where did all water come from originally in the solar system?

When I was speaking on the telephone with NASA's head of Propulsion, Power and Energy, Dr. Earl Van Landingham about Dr. Bogan Maglich's nuclear fusion device, I decided to ask him for his position on UFOs. He said he didn't believe intelligent life from another planet could arrive at earth without yielding a very powerful energy signal. This is because Dr. Van Landingham understands that it takes a tremendous amount of energy and a great frequency of energy to travel from one part of the galaxy to another. Our own Milky Way galaxy is 100,000 light years in diameter. It is 50,000 light years from the periphery to the center of our galaxy where there is now presumed to be a black hole. Our solar system is 30,000 light years distance from the center. Dr. Van Landingham said that if any intelligent being from another planet around another star in the galaxy were to even arrive at Earth, the energy it would take to conquer such distances would be so great, the signal would be detectable well in advance of such an arrival.

We know from studying the model of light as energy that for any proposed UFO to be travelling from another star system it would have to be radiating an energy in the visible or invisible range of light.

So far, Dr. Louis A. Frank's discovery fits that model. He has observed objects, which he calls "small comets" that are only observable in the UV range of light energy. Preceding his discovery, there has never been a comet of any density that is not detectable in the visible light range while simultaneously in the infrared.

While Dr. Louis A. Frank is calling his discovery "small comets," few other scientists agree with him. We will find out more about his discovery later.

If NASA knows the same simple facts I am revealing here, wouldn't you think that they may hypothesize the same: that perhaps this is a sign that Dr. Frank's SOMETHING could posses the kind of energy it takes to conquer light speeds? If that were true, we would expect some kind of a National Security response. Perhaps Dr. Joseph Nuth, III, NASA head of astrochemistry revealed that there was a search by American National Security agencies for these objects on their satellites. The last sentence in paragraph one suggests it: "Yet no other satellite has ever seen evidence for these objects. This includes a vast array of DOD (Department of Defense) satellites as well as far as I can learn." If the Department of Defense was even looking for them on their satellites, there must have been a deeper investigation into Dr. Frank's discovery than we know.

IV - THE VIDEO ARRIVES

According to NASA's "Space Act" signed on July 29, 1958, section 102 (c) (a), we read: "Information obtained or developed by the Administrator in the performance of his functions under this act shall be available for public inspection except: a) information authorized or required by Federal statute to be withheld, and b) information classified to protect the national security."

Everything NASA discovers is supposed to be available to the public and is public domain, except "information, which becomes classified to protect national security." We can assume that UFOs would be considered a national security threat until the Nation's of the world either deemed such visitations as friendly or antagonistic.

In Dr. Nuth's third letter to me he gives evidence that national security satellites did get involved in the search for Dr. Louis A. Frank's mysterious "SOMETHING," as Dr. Nuth wrote, "No other satellite has ever seen evidence of these objects. This includes a vast array of DOD (Department of Defense) satellites as far as I can learn."

We know from the NASA Space Act that if they did find other evidence, it would become instantly "classified." That would mean that the only way to discover if there really was a mysterious anomaly or UFO visiting Earth, we would have to apply a scientific sense of observation from a number of advanced observation tools. The videotape I was about to receive may have that evidence on it, but it would not be easy to make assumptions without the observation tools discussed in the previous chapter.

Mike Boyle finally contacted Martyn Stubbs, the owner of the NASA video revealing the strange and unidentified objects observed on recent 1990s space shuttle missions. He told Mr. Stubbs that he knew a man in Los Angeles who wanted to show his tape around the scientific community for an investigation. Mr. Stubbs was interested. I was given his phone number.

I phoned Martyn Stubbs in 1996. He was a little nervous about who I might be. There was some fear in his voice that I might be from the National Security Agency, I thought. He told me about how he had recorded over 400 hours of NASA's live broadcasts via satellite while he was Program Manager of a local cable TV station. He started to witness strange, unidentified flying objects passing by the space shuttle environment. He then searched the tapes scrutinizing them for more evidence of these objects. They were not all the same. Now he had a library of NASA phenomenon that would certainly make the world curious if they could see for their own eyes. He even told me that the astronauts actually made comments about the objects as they passed by. He said he would prepare me a tape, but he would not meet me in person. He made the tape and I went to the TV station to pick it up in an envelope. When I played it on my television VCR, I was astounded at the physics and movements of these objects.

What if we found out that American, European, Canadian and Russian astronauts travelling on space shuttle missions and missions to the Russian Space Station MIR have encountered intelligent life from other dimensions and civilizations of our universe, and that deep level scientific investigations and National Security measures are being taken by world governments as these contacts continue to intensify as we move into the New Millennium? The video was perhaps revealing all of this to be true.

V - HIGH-SPEED LEFT ANGLE TURN SEQUENCE

This new and exclusive NASA video footage discovered by Martyn Stubbs, first shows a scene where a brightly glowing object escapes the earth's gravity at a very high velocity. Second, in the upper left hand corner of the screen, we see a bright star-like object, which makes a high velocity, sudden left-angle 75 degree turn and is followed by another object that does not make such a turn. At the same time, in the center of the screen, we see a star-like object jump from one point in space to another and stop. At the same time, we see a few meteor-like objects moving in a curved fashion over the Earth's atmosphere.

The physics in this single scene alone would baffle any astrophysicist or astrochemist to the point of a nervous break-down, I thought. The first object I was looking at appeared to be a bright small comet or meteor that was travelling at a speed too slow to be a comet, meteor or shooting star, but more astounding, it was leaving the earth's atmosphere, travelling on a trajectory of about 35 degrees away from the zero plane of earth. This clearly indicating it defied the laws of gravity. It also had a long and luminous tail. The image was being broadcast via satellite using the shuttle's black and white "low light level cameras," NASA tells, "because of their ability to see objects in low light more clearly than the color cameras."

It must be made absolutely clear that no natural object can escape Earth's powerful gravity once it is anywhere near the vicinity of its gravity field, not even a piece of dust. This object was defying that almighty law. What could it be? So far, this didn't fit the description of Dr. Louis A. Frank's discovery of small comets impacting Earth's atmosphere. This was leaving Earth's atmosphere. It was also big and very brightly lit. Even a small comet could not escape Earth's gravity. Whatever this object was, because it defied the laws of gravity, one would have to assume that it had internal energy in it. This is because it takes energy to escape Earth's gravity. For any unidentified object to have internal energy would imply either a new and phenomenal discovery in the solar system, some kind of intelligent space craft, or an unexplainable living organism in space that has its own internal energy. The possibilities were not endless. That is because in the realm of possibilities, all natural objects are eliminated. This would have to be some kind of an unnatural phenomenon.

When I played and replayed the video several times to study just this one incident, I started to see other impossible astrophysics. The assumed meteors moving over the circumference of the Earth's surface were visible for too long, I thought, to be shooting stars.

Dr. Nuth wrote in a February 22, 1999 letter to me of this fact: "Most meteors have velocities greater than 20 kilometers per second – some travel slower, most travel faster – so the amount of time they would appear on video tape would be very brief and those entering the atmosphere would flare, the fade away very rapidly unless they were reasonably massive (~kg)."

I had witnessed hundreds of shooting stars in the night sky and their tails remain visible for what seem to be a fraction of a second only: they burn out and disintegrate into the atmosphere or impact on the Earth's surface. What Dr. Nuth was saying was perfectly clear. But these trails didn't seem to reach a burn-out, rather they had a continuous streaking across the space above the Earth.

The first observation that is alarming about the meteor-like object on this NASA video is that it does not flare and dissipate as a small meteorite would. It keeps on moving over what (by calculations) appears to be over 1,000 miles of the Earth's space surface in 4 seconds. It does not flare and fade away in just a few short miles like most meteorites would. Using Dr. Nuth's analysis, if this were a meteorite, it would have to be quite massive in size, as he states, "…. would flare, then fade away very rapidly unless they were reasonably massive (~kg)."

Assuming the space shuttle is at ~300 miles above the earth (NASA data), and the object was just above the top of the Earth's atmosphere ~100 miles), the object should not even be visible unless it was quite large (over 1 kilometer in size). It is too difficult to see objects even tens of meters across from 200 miles away. This point is easy to understand. This is why the object had to be very large. It may even have been a few miles in diameter. If it really was a meteorite, it would have impacted with the Earth with such force, everyone on the planet would have known that we were struck. The effects would have been devastating.

On June 30, 1908, such a small meteorite struck the Earth in Siberia. It had an estimated diameter of 70 meters. This would still be too small to be observable as a meteorite from ~200 miles above (as in the NASA video). Nevertheless, when the 70-meter sized meteorite struck Siberia, it flattened more than 2,000 square kilometers of forest. The explosion and shock-wave knocked farmers to the ground hundreds of kilometers away from the blast zone. The explosion was equivalent to a 30-megaton nuclear warhead. The nuclear blast that struck Hiroshima in 1945 was only 13 kilotons.

Written by the U.S. House of Representatives, the following clause was entered into the NASA authorization Bill of July 20, 1994:

To the extent practicable, the National Aeronautics and Space Administration, in coordination with the Department of Defense and the space agencies of other countries, shall identify and catalogue within 10 years the orbital characteristics of all comets and asteroids that are greater than 1 kilometer in diameter and are in an orbit around thee Sun that crosses the orbit of Earth.

The reasons for the bill are clear: The magnitude of explosions and potential for human loss of such massive meteorites is a grave threat to humankind. The magnitude of explosions from massive meteorites only 70 meters in diameter are so disastrous, it would be impossible to miss the alleged meteorite in the NASA video if it were actually a meteorite. That is because, by astrophysics calculations on minimum size of the object, it would produce a massive explosion upon impact. If it was a meteorite, it would not have escaped Earth's gravity and it would have impacted upon the surface of the Earth. There were no recorded incidents of such a massive explosion anytime during these NASA missions or after to date.

While the object in this section of the NASA video looks like a meteorite, it has even more stunning characteristics to suggest it was not a meteorite. In the video, the object appeared to travel over a few thousand miles of the Earth's surface (above the surface) in, I counted, four seconds. Wait a minute, I thought. That is incredible speed. I decided to cut the distance traveled in half to be more conservative.

The object I was counting to move over approximately and very conservatively (estimate) at least 1,000 miles of the Earth's 24,000-mile circumference in 4-seconds, clearly moves in a curvature relative to that of the Earth; and disappears over the far horizon. The significance of the curvature of the object's movement relative to the curvature of the Earth is of paramount importance, but when the object disappears exactly at the horizon it is even more conclusive: the object is moving over the Earth's curvature and is not moving over empty space far above. Therefore, its relativity to the Earth could be used to calculate approximate speed.

I did some simple math using relativity of the object traveling over a minimum of 1,000 miles of the Earth's surface in four seconds. First, I took 1,000 miles and divided it by four seconds to see how fast this object was traveling per second. It comes to an absolutely astounding 250 miles per second. To figure out how many miles per hour this object was traveling, I took 250 miles per second times 60 seconds per minute to see how fast this object was traveling per minute. It comes to 15,000 miles per minute; multiplied by 60 minutes in an hour, the speed comes to an unprecedented 900,000 mph. Because the space shuttle is travelling in near opposite direction of the phenomenal object at approximately 17,000 mph (NASA data), I would have to subtract this from the total speed of the object. This left a total approximate speed for the object of 883,000 mph.

No natural object in the history of air flight, space flight, shooting star, asteroid, meteor or comet has a velocity anywhere near this speed. Meteors travel at approximately 12.5 miles per second (According to NASA) or 45,000 mph. The object witnessed on this portion of the tape was traveling 20 times faster than a meteor's average speed. Dr. Louis A. Frank's discovery of hypothesized "small comets" suggests a speed of 35,000 mph. According to NASA, the space shuttle maintains a speed just above 17,000 miles per hour to sustain itself in orbit around the Earth. It makes orbits around the Earth in approximately 90 minutes.

Using time, distance and speed, not only does this object disqualify as a meteor, shooting star or Dr. Louis A. Frank "small comet," it tops any speed of natural and unnatural aircraft or spacecraft known to humankind and science. At 250 miles per second, it could orbit the Earth's circumference (at the equator) of 24,000 miles in 96 seconds. At 250 miles per second, it could fly the 1,000 miles distance between Vancouver, Canada and San Francisco, California in 4 seconds compared to the 2.5-hour flight it takes to fly the same distance by Airline.

This had to be some kind of a craft or phenomenon that was utilizing nuclear propulsion systems to obtain such a speed, such as high-energy antiprotons or a gravity generator. The best rocket fuels on Earth could never propel a craft through space anywhere near this speed. But where could such a craft be coming from if NASA hadn't already developed advanced nuclear propulsion systems for spacecraft?

One could only assume that such craft would have to be either from an Earth-based alternative space program sequestered from the public in research facilities such as Area-51 in Nevada or from an extraterrestrial civilization.

For now, I had only observed one small fragment of Martyn Stubbs' video and I was tossed into a scientific vertigo that may never let me down unless I could be proved wrong. The only way to do that would be to prove to me that my assumptions on distances of the object traveled over the 4-second time period were greatly exaggerated. To

the contrary I knew, I even made my assumptions greatly modest. The distance I used was less than half what I really thought it was.

When I compared the data from this object with a hypothesis that using 18 MeV anti-protons as Dr. Earl Van Landingham (NASA Director for Propulsion, Power and Energy) had said could "allow spacecraft to do 1/10th the speed of light," the object was well within the limits and capabilities of this kind of technology.   One-tenth the speed of light (186,282 miles per second) in miles per hour comes to over 67 million miles per hour.   The UFO was traveling at approximately 883,000 miles per hour, still a fraction of what 18 MeV anti-protons could accomplish . In theory, we have not yet eliminated another possibility: that this object was a very advanced Earth-based "Black Ops" spacecraft.

When we consider the facts that the space shuttle is at 300 miles above the Earth and the UFO was probably 200 miles below creating a burn effect as it flies through the top of the Earth's atmosphere (100 miles), then we must accept the fact that this UFO is very large in size. Because we could not even see a 747 jetliner from even 10 miles away, and this object was clearly visible from 200 miles away, the UFO must have been extremely large: maybe over a mile wide. That would indicate that it is highly unlikely to be from Earth.

VI - HUBBLE REPAIR MISSION SEQUENCE

I now watched another segment of the Martyn Stubbs NASA video. This segment showed two astronauts repairing the Hubble Space telescope. There was a small flashing light passing slowly behind them in the background. At first it appears as though it may be a piece of space debris. Space debris is just old junk from earlier space missions and satellites that is drifting through space and slowly falling towards the earth. It is usually no more than a few inches in size. This was obviously not space debris from an earlier mission because any debris from an earlier mission would have already fallen into a much lower altitude orbit. According to NASA, the space shuttle orbits the earth at about 300 miles above the earth. The top of the atmosphere is at 100 miles. Space starts above the top of the atmosphere.

The astronauts actually comment on the phenomenon as we can hear them on the video, "It looks like you got an object right in front of you Mark. Are you looking out there?" Mark answers, "Never mind." Someone comments, "It's about your 10:00, 11:00 going away. Don't worry about it." Then another person comments, as if they have the answer, "Yeah, we think the camera filter came off Mark." Another part of the video shows a close-up on the space shuttle's video camera and how well the filters and lens are concealed: there is no possibility of the filter unscrewing, breaking past another layer of glass and then drifting out into space. NASA was clearly lying here, but to protect the viewer from what fact? What does NASA know about these mysterious objects? Why do they lie to the public?

The astronauts do not appear to be worried, as though they had previously witnessed such space phenomenon. The other possibility, I thought, is that they could have all been briefed as to expect certain space phenomenon and not to react suddenly on live broadcasts to the world. This astronaut could not help but comment.

If the unidentified flying object phenomenon were seen as a National Security threat to astronauts in space, would we expect to see a Star Wars laser retaliating a strike against them? In this case we do not. The object is drifting by in the background acting non-intrusively. There were too many reasons why it seemed that the astronauts had prior briefing and knowledge about these alleged UFOs. If they were guided by extraterrestrial civilizations, they didn't appear to pose any military threat. If the object were a satellite, you would also think that they could both see that and recognize that as a fact. The astronaut does not call the object a satellite. He calls it an "object."

VII - RUSSIAN SPACE STATION MIR SEUENCE

This section of the Martyn Stubbs, NASA video requires a lot of replaying and knowledge before anyone can observe it for flaws. It shows the NASA space shuttle black and white cameras looking for the Russian Space Station MIR. They cannot seem to find it because there are so many other objects out in the near space environment that are preventing the shuttle crew from distinguishing the MIR from the surrounding objects. These background objects, we are told by ground control operators and shuttle crew members, are stars. The surrounding objects are also moving (stars cannot move), some very slowly and others seem to accelerate like shooting stars.

The first odd occurrence in this section of the NASA video is that at an assumed altitude of 300 miles above the earth, there should not be an enormity of objects around or even within a few thousand miles of the Russian Space Station. We are told that the background objects are stars but can easily understand that stars do not change positions and drift off course as many of these objects appear to be doing. Because they are just white amorphous looking balls, it is difficult to say what they are. A trained observer can easily deduct that they are not stars. The sequence goes on for around ten minutes and the astronauts and ground control operators never seem to be able to be conclusive about where the MIR really is.

The second questionable phenomenon on this part of the video is the fact that the space shuttle is supposed to be at 300 miles above the earth. The top of the earth's atmosphere is at 100 miles (NASA data). We are told that there are a number of shooting stars and meteors going by as the crew and ground control look for the MIR.

Meteors are usually small objects that burn up and disintegrate as they enter the earth's atmosphere. They usually streak, burn up and disappear as they disintegrate. These supposed meteors and shooting stars do not burn up and disintegrate. They just keep on passing by leaving a streak behind them: possibly just a video drag trail due to slow video frames per second. Some of these shooting stars come from far away in space and race towards the earth's atmosphere visible in the video frame below.

Now, using the logic that the shuttle is at 300 miles above the earth, and the fact that the top of the earth's atmosphere is at 100 miles, 200 miles below the shuttle, why are meteors burning up and becoming visible at all? Shooting stars and most meteors are so small, that as they pass through space, do not appear visible to the human eye or camera until they enter the earth's atmosphere. The problem with this picture is they could not be burning up while they are clearly 200 miles or greater above the top of the earth's atmosphere. That is because there are no particles in the void of space to cause the friction needed to create a meteoric burn.

There were many other incidents on the video that showed fluffy, house-sized objects passing closely by the MIR. These were so similar in description to Dr. Louis A. Frank's "Small Comet" discovery, they just might be the same phenomenon, I thought. For now, I had very little data on Dr. Frank's discovery. That would all arrive later in the investigation.

NASA assumed that its observers were not paying attention to scientific facts and could once again divert its viewers from the possibility that something else was moving through space above the earth, not shooting stars. Also, the objects surrounding the MIR would not be stars or shooting stars because they were moving much too slow to be shooting stars.

I decided to send Dr. Nuth at NASA the video of the preceding sequences we have just reviewed in the summer of 1998. At that time, I was working as an executive at a small U.S. Defense Contractor called HiEnergy Microdevices, building a leading-edge technology for the detection of buried landmines, narcotics, explosives and chemical weapons. I was deeply involved in work and communicating with the Department of Defense about this more serious issue. I had left the UFO investigation of the NASA video in the back of my mind. By now, Dr. Nuth at NASA should have answered me, but he didn't. I thought he just might be unable to speak, as his opinions were respected and credible. That would mean he would have to come up with a credible answer to an unexplainable event.

As for Russian evidence, in the 1993, I attended a party that Dr. Bogdan Maglich, the nuclear fusion scientist I was an associate of, was having at his home in Laguna Beach, California. The party was to welcome Russian scientists who were part of the Department of Energy and Department of Defense's plan to convert Russian nuclear weapon's scientists into peaceful research. This program was designed to offset the possibility of desperate Russian scientists taking jobs in rogue nations that might hire them to build nuclear weapons. The program was a failure. The DOE and DOD didn't spend the money.

In the party, I met a man called "Nikolai" who was the head of the whole Russian Space Program at the time. He didn't speak English. Through an interpreter (a young Russian woman), I asked him if the Russian cosmonauts had ever seen UFOs. He laughed but answered my question, "We have never seen anything like that. If the cosmonauts had seen UFOs, I would be the first one to know about it."

I then proceeded to tell Nikolai the story of the UFO I saw in Berkeley, California in 1968. I told him there were over 100 witnesses to the event. He then told me that it must have been a mass hallucination. I laughed at his sense of humor but I also knew he didn't want me to know or believe in UFOs.

Nikolai then proceeded to tell me a story of an alleged strange sighting of a green ball of light that was seen to fall from the sky and go under the water in a lake in northern Russia. The story fascinated me. Someone in Russia reported the story to the government. Nikolai's point was that it was not a UFO, rather a strange phenomenon that might be mistaken for a UFO. He had heard of many other incidents like it, all of which could be explained as "ball lightning" or other plasma effects caused by nature. He then gave me his business card and said to call him if I ever got videotape or pictures of real UFOs. I kept that business card for years and then one day lost it. I lost it before I could send him video of the Russian Space Station MIR sequence I had just witnessed.

But there has been some evidence from the Russian astronauts saying that they had seen "flying saucers" on recent missions to MIR. A Russian Cosmonaut named Alexandr Baladin stated at a UFO convention that "flying saucers" have come into close proximity to the MIR space station as well as the Baikonur Cosmodrom.

He added there is sufficient evidence to warrant a scientific study of the phenomenon, and that it is time that world governments officially acknowledge the UFO phenomenon's existence.

Baladin disclosed December 23, 1998, during an International Ufology Forum in Brazil, that he and fellow cosmonaut Musa Manarov had seen UFOs. During docking operations between his space capsule and the MIR, Baladin saw a glowing object a short distance away. Could these be the same lights that are being witnessed on this NASA Russian Space Station MIR sequence? They certainly fit the same descriptions.

Musa Manarov captured the UFOs on videotape that was shown during the UFO congress in Brazil. Baladin claimed that the recording and other evidence presented during the Congress, "must be studied by an international scientific commission." Musa Manarov didn't know what I was up to. I had a whole panel of physicists looking into this phenomenon but the answers would take time.

Why were Russian Cosmonauts coming forward to tell their stories while American Astronauts wouldn't breathe a word? Was the Soviet Union more excited about sharing information on intelligent contact with extraterrestrials with the world than Americans? By the examples these Russian Cosmonauts were setting, it should be no surprise that Americans were being duped by their own space administration.

VIII - NASA UFOS DEBATED ON TV

A scientist named Jack Kasher went public with some interesting NASA UFO video footage by presenting alleged sightings in an NBC 2-hour TV special called "Confirmation, The Hard Evidence of Aliens Among Us?" It aired on February 17, 1999. A portion of the documentary was dedicated to Dr. Kasher's NASA UFOs.

The main focus was a very small point of fuzzy light that had to be magnified to reveal that the point of light made a sudden directional change and went shooting out into space. UFO researchers and Dr. Kasher believed they were seeing evidence of a spacecraft conducting a hyper-velocity turn and bolt out into space away from the earth. His physics all made sense.

Within days of the NBC broadcast of "Confirmation," Congress ordered hearings into the matter and suddenly NASA had official press statements suggesting that the alleged NASA UFOs were nothing other than dust or debris in shuttle environment. When the shuttle's altitude and directional thrusters were fired, the pieces of debris go shooting off giving the illusion of being distant unidentified flying objects. That was the end of the public perception of what Jack Kasher had to show the world. Regardless of NASA's statements to the press, there were still many researchers who didn't trust the government or NASA.

I knew that the Martyn Stubbs NASA video I had already seen was far better than anything presented on "Confirmation" by Jack Kasher. Even so, my partner in this project, photographer Mike Boyle didn't think that Martyn Stubbs had given us his best footage at all. In fact, Mike Boyle was feeling betrayed by Stubbs, and that for us to make a proper investigation, we needed the better footage. I thought, of course Martyn Stubbs didn't give us his best footage. He barely knows who we are. We would just have to wait and see.

The day after the NBC show "Confirmation" aired on NBC, February 18, 1999, I received a letter from Dr. Joseph Nuth, III at NASA about the video I sent him last summer. He was now taking the identical position that NASA took against the NBC show "Confirmation" as though I were receiving a carbon copy memo of what NASA had told the press. It reads as follows:

> Dear Mr. Sereda, I did look carefully at the video you sent and I really must apologize to you for not replying sooner. The objects that were on the video appear to me to be floating debris from the cargo bay of the space shuttle. These objects often appeared to be fuzzy because they got quite close to the camera and were often out of focus. Because they were so close, they also appear to travel at high speed and any minor disturbance within the shuttle environment (outgassing, firing of attitude control thrusters, etc.) is magnified enormously - thus the rapid turns. The spotty illumination and shadowing in the bay can also make objects suddenly appear or disappear. I saw a wealth

of similar debris come up off the floor and out of many minor crevices during microgravity flights on the KC-135. The space shuttle is a notoriously "dirty" environment by any laboratory standards. That's why they always close up any shuttle serviced by the shuttle well before it gets too near. This is especially true for satellites such as HST with high precision optics. Again, I do apologize for not responding sooner.

Joe Nuth

It seemed to me that NASA was now under some public and political fire to either admit they were witnessing unidentified flying objects in space or come up with some plausible theory to explain it.

The objects in the video, High-Speed Left Angle Turn Sequence, were clearly too bright to be pieces of dust in front of a camera lens. The brightly glowing object moving uniformly over the curvature of the earth at approximately 900,000 mph and then disappearing at exactly the point the object should (the horizon) does not suggest the physics and movement of a piece of dust. The chances of dust behaving so perfectly while it is between a camera lens and the earth are billions to one.

The very luminescent object leaving the earth's atmosphere prior to the high-speed angular turn is much too bright to be a mere piece of dust. Dr. Nuth must have been under some orders from above to cover something up, just as stated in the Space Act.

During the Hubble repair mission, when the two astronauts engage in a short conversation about, "There's an object right in front of you Mark, are you looking out there," they couldn't be talking about a piece of dust or debris floating from the shuttle. Such garbage does not warrant curiosity and conversation while you are focusing on repairing a damaged telescope. The way NASA lies and tells us that "the camera filter must have come off" (another impossibility) suggest a distraction for the public to forget the object out there. If the object were dust, why go through all the trouble to distract and lie to the public?

When I tested the theory that near-field "floating debris" could cause such illusions, with a good quality digital video camera, the results astounded me once again. With a 3-CCD chip in my digital camera (NASA only uses the best quality), the depth of field was so phenomenal, while focused on a city skyline over 3 miles away in the background, a key remained undistorted and perfectly in-focus on 4 inches in front of the camera.

I did another test with the camera focused on a large tree approximately 200 feet away while I passed a set of keys only 4 inches in front of the camera. Both the tree and the keys remained perfectly in-focus at the same time. This means that both the extreme near and far points being in focus, nothing in between those points could possibly go out of focus.

So the NASA theory that near-field objects should appear out-of-focus and fuzzy did not hold at all. The NASA theory said that the fuzzy orb around the near-field object resembles a UFO disc-shape and can therefore be an optical illusion. But as CCD imaging in professional digital video cameras provides such good depth of field, this could not happen and NASA's Number One argument falls apart.

In at least one piece of NASA video I examined from Space shuttle mission STS-80, I could see the camera's amazing depth of field in action. It was focused on the Earth's surface some 300 miles away while at the same time a piece of dust or smudge mark on the shuttle's window pane was in perfect focus at the same time. This again means that nothing in between those two points could possibly be out of focus. Yet in the footage, there was a round, translucent disc-shaped object moving from the foreground and far into the background. It had to be a UFO.

This was evidence that when Dr. Joseph Nuth, III wrote in his fourth letter to me that, "The objects that were on the video appear to be floating debris from the cargo bay of the space shuttle. These objects often appeared to be fuzzy because they got quite close to the camera and were often out of focus."

I was so outraged at NASA for lying to me, I decided to use the freedom of Information Act and write Dr. Nuth requesting all NASA files and videotape of these objects for my own record. The Freedom of Information Act requires that any public government agency release public information. But as the 1958, NASA Space Act reveals, "NASA doesn't have to release information classified to protect the national security."

While I was waiting to get an answer from the FOIA request from NASA, I wrote Dr. Nuth by e-mail again. The letter is as follows:

> Dear Dr. Nuth, III, I received your e-mail today. It seems you have made a radical turn opposing your previous views of these mysterious objects. How could the objects in the video be "floating debris" when the NASA commentators are calling them "meteors?" Also, if they were floating debris, why would one astronaut be commenting to another that "Mark, there's an object about ten o, clock to your left?" I do not believe the astronauts would comment on floating debris. Also, you say that the objects accelerate because of shuttle bursts, bursts of light which do not appear in my video. If shuttle bursts caused the objects to make radical shifts in direction, they would not make such precise angular turns and have a perfect line of trajectory? Also, shuttle bursts against debris would cause all debris to respond in an identical or similar fashion of movement. In this video, there are several objects moving in different directions both low and high in the earth's atmosphere. I do not propose that the objects are UFOs, but rather mysterious objects. Your prior e-mails to me were intelligent answers. This latest e-mail suggests fear and denial of obvious facts. You are a doctorate in astrophysics, yes? Such a man would not make statements that were illogical to his profession, unless he was under stress. Why are you answering me with such illogical propaganda? NASA is a public and government agency. What do you have to hide? I just wish to know the truth, but perhaps you will not tell me more than you have.

At this point, I was either in trouble with Dr. Nuth for expressing so much distrust in NASA and the investigation and conversations with him over, or I would prompt him to be more honest with me. He answered me in his fifth letter as follows:

> Mr. Sereda:

On the very few occasions when my integrity has been questioned in the past, it has always been by someone who both did not know me well and who also did not like what I had to say. This appears to be the case here as well. Just to set things straight, I do not really care if the images in the video that you sent are house-sized meteors or hair balls from a cosmic cat. The latter might be more interesting to some, but neither will have even a small effect on my own research. The thought of a NASA conspiracy is ludicrous to anyone that has even a passing association with the people in this agency. As an example, the footage that so disturbs you was freely broadcast by NASA to the world. I doubt very much that this is an approved method of keeping secrets. If you want an opinion concerning a scientific matter, I have freely given it in the past. If you just want someone to agree with you, I suggest that you buy a parrot.

Several of the things written below let me know that you misunderstood some of the things I wrote. Others let me know that you haven't the smallest idea of what a meteor's orbit might be – or how it would look entering the earth's atmosphere. As an exercise, I'd suggest that you count the number of objects between the earth and the shuttle (assume an altitude of ~300 mi. and that the top of the atmosphere is at ~100 mi.), use this to calculate a "space density" for these objects. Multiply this space density by the mass of the objects to figure the influx of material to the surface of the Earth. Or, use this density to figure the time for the shuttle or an average satellite to be struck by one of these objects. Not only is the mass flux much too high to ignore, but no satellite has a chance of surviving days, let alone years if these were actually meteors.

I thought this was funny because Dr. Nuth still thinks that I assume that Dr. Louis A. Frank's "small comets" and the objects in the video are actually meteors. This is why he felt I misunderstood him. I didn't know what else to call them. Because he believes I am suggesting that they are meteors (as NASA commentators in the video called some of them), he was giving me reasons as to why they could not be as such. We had already eliminated meteors a long time ago, I thought.

Chapter Three
The Alternative Space Program Theory

"The point of philosophy is to start with something so simple as not to seem worth stating, and to end with something so paradoxical that no one will believe it" – Bertrand Russell

I – Two Space Programs?

The general theory of "The Alternative Space Program" is that NASA and the Russian Space Programs are utilizing what the public believes to be the most advanced technology applied to space travel. Those programs are believed to be a decoy acting as an illusion for the public while the super advanced Alternative Space Program is sequestered for use of members of secret societies. The Alternative Space Program theory alleges that humans have already manned flights to all of the planets and may have bases on Mars, the moon and other planets in the solar system.

If there really is an Alternative Space Program, there would have to be proof of the development of an energy source and propulsion system capable of surpassing the developments used by NASA and the Russian space programs.

Many witnesses claim to have seen UFOs flying above the skies of Groom Lake near Nellis Air Force Base in Nevada. Some of the flying objects appear as points of light in the sky that make sudden jumps through space at incredible speeds.

Since rocketry could not allow such incredible speeds, nuclear propulsion systems would be the next alternative to explain what was happening in the skies above Area-51. But what kind of nuclear research has been going on in Nevada? The world has had its eyes on the Nevada nuclear test site since the first nuclear test in New Mexico on July 5, 1945.

There was no doubt that the evidence in the Martyn Stubbs' collection of NASA videos was suggesting UFOs, and had some amazing characteristics of UFOs, the evidence was not conclusive. Most of my scientific questions to Dr. Nuth had obviously been ignored by him, which suggested he was trying to distract me back to the meteor debate. Because we had already eliminated meteors, I didn't understand why he was going back to that point and obviating the questions I posed. His distraction was enough evidence for me to hypothesize a cover-up at NASA.

Because Dr. Nuth's new answers were so identical to the ones Congress and the press had for the NBC "Confirmation, The Hard Evidence of Aliens Among Us," and its NASA UFO scenes, I thought it was all too coordinated looking by the agency. I didn't believe it.

I still needed evidence so conclusive, that even NASA couldn't argue it. It needed NASA UFO footage that could prove that the objects on the tape were not "floating debris." I would eventually get that evidence and more from Martyn Stubbs, but for now, I had a long way to go. Martyn Stubbs had his best footage locked away and he didn't trust my integrity yet.

Mike Boyle was still suspecting that Martyn had better footage that he was hiding from us. I needed it to go on with the investigation at NASA. The footage I had was good, but not the Holy Grail of the research I was looking for. The Holy Grail would be footage from any government agency that revealed undeniable proof of contact with an extraterrestrial civilization.

I awaited my freedom of Information Act request from Dr. Nuth, which I believed would be a NASA video library and documents with black marks all over them hiding the truth. I would have to wait.

Because propulsion systems for spacecraft require infinite amounts of energy to reach greater velocities, to find out if there really is an alternative space program sequestered on our very own planet Earth for secret societies, we would have to find out if science has discovered an advanced energy source. And, if an advanced energy source were discovered, why weren't we using it to solve the serious current environmental energy pollution crisis?

Dr. Steven Greer is the Director of CSETI, Center for the Study of Extraterrestrial Intelligence, and leads a working team of some 200 CSETI members and associates, government employee witnesses, consultants and government contacts. Dr. Greer has briefed and been briefed by government and U.N. officials on the subject of unidentified objects in U.S. airspace, is convinced that the materials and technology of UFOs may have the answer to solving the energy pollution crisis. He believes much of modern technology owes itself to reverse engineered, crashed UFOs such as the alleged Roswell incident in New Mexico on July 5, 1947. I always thought it was strange that a flying saucer would crash on the same day anniversary of the first nuclear weapons test in history and in the same State where that test was conducted on July 5, 1945.

If UFOs were really spacecraft capable of light speed and or beyond it and reverse engineered, the technology would theoretically allow for our own space program, alternative or NASA's, to grow exponentially. If such a discovery were made, according to NASA's Space Act of 1958, section 102, "NASA is charged with the making available to agencies directly concerned with national defense of discoveries that have military value or significance…" Military technology would also grow exponentially.

Dr. Greer feels that environmental pollution and the cost to service gas to 6 billion people worldwide can be dramatically reduced by implementing reverse engineered UFO energy technology.

If UFOs are travelling beyond light speed or near it to arrive at Earth from other star systems, then the source of their energy must truly have the answer to the energy pollution crisis we face here on earth today. He believes the secret government and alternative space program does exist and that they are hiding this technology from the world just to keep themselves in an elite status of control over the masses.

II – It Takes Alternative Energy To Conquer Alternative Space

What is currently happening with the world's efforts to develop environmentally safe and abundant nuclear energy? In 1939, Albert Einstein wrote a now famous letter to President Roosevelt urging the development of uranium fission for the purpose of building a bomb that could end World War II. After the July 5, 1945, A-bomb test in New Mexico, Einstein's hairstyle changed drastically from lying flat on his head to a style that resembled the world's first nuclear explosion. He would never be the same. Although he didn't build the bomb with his own hands, his mind power created a catastrophic revolution in warfare and electrical energy production. That August, his plan bore more deadly fruit: Hiroshima and Nagasaki disappeared under mushroom clouds leaving an estimated 70-100,000 casualties. The nature of war and civilization changed forever, and his attitude about what he had set into motion changed, too; he became a spiritual prototype for scientists and scholars world-wide. The media focused on Einstein despite constructive minds like Nikola Tesla having warned the world against splitting the atom.

Tesla invented clean energy: the alternating current generators and transmission systems for electricity (first installed at the Westinghouse Niagara Falls power plant), which made America an industrial superpower. Ironically, Tesla remains little known, while Einstein, whose theory of relativity made us a nuclear superpower, became a household word. After the war, keeping the weapon's program alive became such an urgent priority that that the Soviet Union and the United States sought to end all research into non-radioactive nuclear energy. The Atomic Energy Commission (AEC), now the Department of Energy (DOE), gave orders to "stop the new technology from destroying the weapon's fuel program," fearing that when utility companies learned that a non-radioactive miniature power source was feasible, they would buy it and put it on line for the public, denying the Department of Defense its supply of weapons-grade plutonium produced by radioactive nuclear power plants.

The point is, non-radioactive nuclear power plants were incapable of producing plutonium from uranium.

In 1932, seven years before Einstein's letter to the President, John Cockroft and Ernest T.S. Walton demonstrated the first energy-producing nuclear reaction. Four years later, their achievement won them the Nobel Prize. Less well known is that their process for producing nuclear energy was non-radioactive (accomplished by bombarding lithium with protons). Facts like these lie hidden for decades simply because public-school textbooks omit them along with many minor but important details.

The DOE boasts a 45-year old, H-bomb-based fusion program, which monopolizes all government fusion funding. The DOE's fusion machine, housed in Princeton University's Plasma Physics Lab to keep a low profile, is a continuation of top-secret cold-war research on the use of fusion for massive production of plutonium and tritium for nuclear weapons.

The Tokomak fusion machine, the media tells us, is supposed to supply the future of humankind with a non-radioactive, safe energy source. That is how the government gained public support for the program. This fusion machine burns tritium, a radioactive H-bomb fuel, which produces horrible neutron radiation, 80 percent of its total energy. The machine is capable of "breeding" 100 times more plutonium than the fission of uranium reactors in use today: it is the fuel machine for the perfect weapon. Utility companies, the ultimate users of new power sources reject the government's "tame the H-bomb" fusion program as unacceptable for public use, not only on the environmental and weapon-proliferation grounds, but also for economic reasons. In 1984, when the DOE rejected the utilities' demand to fund an alternative line of fusion research pioneered by Cockroft and Walton, the Electric Power Research Institute abolished its fusion division in protest. Meanwhile, the news media have depicted this deadly form of fusion as the peaceful, environmental source of energy of the future.

In early May of 1994, Congressman George Brown (D-Calif.), Chairman of the Science, Space and Technology Committee, introduced a new bill. A result of three years of heated television and radio debates and newspaper articles, as well as of congressional hearings with major scientific, political and public personalities, the bill would allow for clean, compact, non-radioactive (neutron-less) fusion energy technologies which would actually compete with the DOE's fusion program weaponry.

Despite previous resistance from the DOE against clean fusion, the "Fusion Energy Research and Development Act" would create a new Office for Alternative Fusion Energy and a separate budget line for alternate fusion technologies. This bill has emerged in tact from Rep. Brown's committee. The next step was to vote on the House floor.

The mastermind and driving force behind both non-radioactive aneutronic fusion and the alternate bill in Congress was Dr. Bogdan Castle Maglich, the high-energy experimental physicist who discovered the omega meson and other particles. In 1961, the omega meson discovery won Maglich and three associates a White House citation from President John F. Kennedy.

Maglich is the inventor of the "autocollider," also known as the "self-collider" or "migma" (Greek for "mixture"), a miniature, non-radioactive fusion machine that demonstrates the principle for a non-radioactive fusion reactor in a 100 cc (approximately 6-cubic-inch) volume. In autocolliders, beams of atoms are made to turn around and collide with themselves, causing them to fuse and generate high-energy charged particles for the conversion to electric power and or possible advanced propulsion systems for spacecraft. For this discovery, the president of the Swiss Confederation made him an Honorary Citizen of Switzerland.

Maglich holds a Ph.D. degree in physics at MIT, was formerly a research team director at CERN (The European Center for high-energy physics) in Geneva and was also professor of physics at the University of Pennsylvania and at Rutgers University. He is founder, president and chief scientist of Advanced Physics Corporation (APC), which spent $26 million in private and $2.5 million in Air Force funds on aneutronic fusion-energy research using the autocollider. While most forms of fusion are radioactive, Maglich's device employs a formula of deuterium+helium-3 that creates a non-radioactive nuclear reaction resulting in more energy output than any nuclear fuel per fuel weight including plutonium.

Using a miniature autocollider, in 1984 his laboratory completed the final research stage. Yet to be funded, the "Demonstration of Energy Production" test was planned to be done in cooperation with major nuclear labs in Russia, under the State Department's "Conversion of Peaceful Nuclear Research" program for Russian weapon scientists.

Maglich flew supporters with him to Washington to speak at a Congressional hearing hoping to sway Congress to a favorable floor vote. I spoke in Congress with him as an environmentalist and Director of the Los Angeles based "Tesla Foundation." Our efforts were defeated by the nuclear-industry lobby. The powers against a nuclear energy source that could solve the environmental energy pollution crisis and propel spacecraft to the far reaches of the solar system in a fraction of today's space flight times were so adverse, I had to deduce a possible conspiracy.

Chairman of the Board at Maglich's APC, Glenn T. Seaborg, had emerged as a possible conspirator sent to the firm to destroy Maglich's clean-fusion efforts from within. A chemist by training, Seaborg shared the Nobel Prize with Edwin MacMillan for discovering plutonium, a key instrument in the Manhattan Project's development of the first atomic bomb and the fuel for all future atomic weapons. Later, Seaborg Chaired the Atomic Energy Commission under Presidents Kennedy, Johnson and Nixon. He was not only important to the Manhattan Project, he was also the main proponent of the nuclear weapons testing in the Nevada desert, despite many attempts by the world's richest man of the time, Howard Hughes, to stop it.

One day I was driving Dr. Glenn Seaborg to the Airport in Orange County after a Board meeting at APC, which I attended. When I asked him about what he knew about Howard Hughes, he just started talking. He said, "Howard Hughes almost stopped our nuclear weapons testing program. He complained so much about the shaking of the casinos in Las Vegas during our testing. And, as you know he was very powerful."

When the richest man in the world wants to interfere with nuclear weapons testing, what happens? National Security and Department of Defense directives are never stopped, although they can be merely thwarted by efforts like Hughes tries to undertake.

The authors of "Next to Hughes," a biography of Howard Hughes, stated in the book that one of the billionaire's aids, John Meir, was being used by Hughes to attempt to bribe presidential candidates (including Richard Nixon and Robert Kennedy) with large sums of money if they promised to end the nuclear weapons testing program once in office.

Hughes allegedly even offered Lyndon Johnson one million dollars after he retired, although Johnson declined. Hughes hired John Meir as his man against the nuclear weapons testing in Nevada.

Not only did I meet with the publishers of "Next to Hughes," I had previously met with Hughes man against nuclear weapons testing, John Meir, who was living in Canada in Exile. Why was he living in Exile? While Meir was trying to hire me to write his life story, he told me:

> The CIA pinned those murder charges on me because of what I knew and what I was going to expose about Watergate, Nixon and Howard Hughes. I saw Howard Hughes before his alleged death, and he was fine. He was not ill. That was some actor they had in there. They flew the real Hughes out in a helicopter and the fake one in an airplane. Someone wanted him dead.

Why would anyone want Hughes dead? I can only assume that Hugh's and his aid John Meir's efforts to stop the nuclear testing in Nevada may have gotten him in a lot of trouble with national Security. But there may be more.

Howard Hughes is the founding father of Hughes Aircraft. He built aircraft and had a keen interest in space flight. Hughes' top executives, Summa Corporation Senior Vice-President Nadine Henley and Executive Vice-President Bill Gay, notified Dr. Maglich that Hughes was keenly interested in funding the development of the non-radioactive nuclear autocollider. Perhaps Hughes thought this might offset the radioactive nuclear bomb program. Perhaps Hughes was also interested in Maglich's work because of what it could mean for fueling advanced space and aircraft. This would have later lead to advanced nuclear propulsion systems for spacecraft, the very business Hughes was in. He was right, but he died (or vanished) before he could sign the check.

Dr. Glenn Seaborg, the man who was Head of the nuclear testing in Nevada, was now Maglich's Chairman of the Board. Amazingly, in 1984 Seaborg approached an astonished Dr. Maglich stating his support of Maglich's research into non-radioactive deuterium+helium-3 fusion. For a day, environmentalists were shaking Seaborg's hand.

It seemed that the staunchest scientific advocate of nuclear power and that "radioactivity is good for you" propaganda school had finally seen the light and reversed himself as the mythological "Darth Vader" in the Hollywood movie "Star Wars" did.

Seaborg stated in a telephone interview with Earth News magazine editor Adam Rogers:

Modern societies do not suffer from an energy crisis. What they suffer from is an energy-residue crisis, which produces millions of tons of radioactive waste and carbon and sulfate emissions from fossil fuel-burning power plants. In view of this, Maglich's approach to fusion may be the answer to the search for environmentally safe energy.

In Defense News (May 1989), Seaborg offered the following quote on the significance of Maglich's autocollider:

Humankind may be at the brink of an energy technology, which is compact, safe and has virtually no residue but the electricity we see fit to produce with it.

Clinton Ashworth, Supervising mechanical engineer for the California based Pacific Gas and Electric, said to me when I interviewed him, "A spaceshuttle full of moon dust has enough helium-3 in it to meet all the energy demands of the United States for one full year." As Dr. Maglich pointed out, "Nine grams of helium-3 holds the energy equivalent to 1,000 barrels of crude oil. An autocollider can breed helium-3 from seawater. You don't need to go to the moon." Who would have ever guessed that moon dust has more energy in it than oil? The only problem with the energy in moon dust, fusion had to be reached in order to extract it.

By 1983, Dr. Maglich's new self-collider led the world in attaining the highest levels of two of the three criteria needed for fusion: a temperature of 10 billion degrees centigrade (1 billion needed to fuse helium-3) and a confinement time of over 20 seconds. The Tokomak government fusion reactor could barely reach 100 million degree temperatures and confinement times of only 1 second. Maglich was leading the way and no one knew his name in mainstream media.

Dr. David Suzuki, host of the Candian-produced public television environmental series called "The Nature of Things," wrote to me about the project: "With Seaborg supporting Maglich's work, he should get his R&D monies." Seaborg was that powerful and influential. But why didn't he use his power to get this project funded?

Before getting involved, the Canadian government waited to see whether the Americans would jump in. In a letter to me from the Canadian Office of Energy, Mines and Resources, I was told: "If the Americans aren't doing anything with aneutronic fusion, then it couldn't be much of anything." Novelist John Le Carre terms this "me too" attitude the "crawling adherence to America." I thought Canadians would always be looking to America for technology and better jobs while it waited in line for a weaker dollar.

It wasn't long before the conspiracy against clean energy reached all the way to Washington and beckoned Dr. Maglich from afar. I had formed a company called "The Green & Blue Corporation" with a wealthy Saudi partner named Ghassan Ibrahim in 1992. He funded our company. We were looking for investors to finance technology that would have a positive impact on the environment and help solve energy pollution. Maglich's project was at the top of our list. Every time we found an investor who was interested, they always confided in and checked with the Department of Energy in Washington for advice. The DOE always turned investors away from making such an investment. Even with Dr. Seaborg and other Nobel Prize winners like Murray Gell-Mann on our side, the answer was always "no" from investors.

A $2.5 million U.S. Air Force feasibility study on Maglich's autocollider as an aneutronic space power source was ordered by Congress in 1987. Maglich subcontracted Bechtel Corporation to produce an engineering design of his clean-fusion space power station. The Air Force did computer feasibility studies on the design on Super Cray IIs (the most advanced simulation computers in the world) to see if Maglich's technology would fail or succeed at reaching its next goal of producing fusion power. The results were classified and called "Ground-breaking" by the Air Force review.

In 1989, just as Maglich made plans to publish the finished design, the Defense Nuclear Agency classified it as "export controlled," a designation forbidding any written or verbal presentation of an invention or concept except to government officials. This blatantly violated an international agreement that forbids withholding information about controlled-fusion energy, but the agency justified it by stating that the design contained "ground-breaking work on fusion power."

James Fletcher, then head of NASA, heard about the work of Dr. Maglich and became interested in funding a prototype because of the potential it had for light weight power source and nuclear propulsion systems for advanced spacecraft. Now NASA was involved and wanted to utilize this technology for its own space program. If NASA could fund it, there would be no reason to suspect a conspiracy by an alternative space program.

Despite many attempts by James Fletcher, then head of NASA and the Air Force to get completion funding for Maglich's technology from Congress, the answer from every administration since Kennedy's has been "no." Since investors stick like glue to DOE decisions, the final answer from investors has been "no" also.

In 1989, Glenn Seaborg spoke in Tokyo declaring the safety of continued radioactive fission power plants. On the issue of safety, Seaborg stated that Chernobyl was a "minor accident." He said the immediate death toll was 32. Significantly, he did not mention uranium mining pollution, accidents, birth defects and most importantly, nuclear-waste handling and disposal. He claimed that nuclear power has offset greenhouse-effect carbon dioxide by 378 million tons worldwide.

Compared to the relatively low cost of finishing R&D on Maglich's non-radioactive nuclear power, the cost of storing nuclear waste makes no sense at all and would be almost needless. A non-radioactive d-helium-3 reactor like Maglich's could produce electricity so inexpensively that hydrogen fuel could be manufactured at a cost competitive with today's gasoline prices. It would be the end of Global Warming, oil spills and air pollution and more. Yet governments, investors and even Greenpeace's nuclear scientist, Dr. Eric Ferscht, refuse to talk to Maglich about financing his solution to the crisis without first getting DOE approval.

By establishing a monopoly on scientific thought, this bureaucratic agency (DOE) can block all breakthroughs in energy research and it has.

The nuclear lobby may have convinced Seaborg that the clean-fusion research should be stopped by throwing Maglich out of his own company. Dr. Maglich has had a damaging effect on the nuclear industry by informing the public and Congress that something better than nuclear power is at hand.

The Industry lobby claimed, "[Maglich] makes us look bad" and said that their own experts knew that "aneutronic fusion is impossible." Their advice was to get APC to drop fusion and commercialize the many inventions from the National Weapon Laboratories. Commercialization would be "a big moneymaker," and Seaborg would see real value in the APC stock given to him by Maglich. Since Maglich had the majority stockholder's vote, the nuclear lobby proposed a coup for takeover of APC. This takeover would achieve two goals: Maglich's threat to the nuclear power and weapons programs would be eliminated, and Seaborg's takeover of APC would steer it toward new endeavors.

On June 25, 1994, APC shareholders received an astounding letter signed by Seaborg. It announced that Maglich had been "indefinitely suspended from the company for cause" (without specifying the cause) and given an indefinite leave without pay, and that he, Seaborg, had received nine million APC shares for his services. Since the shares then sold for $4, Seaborg gave himself stock worth $36 million and 60-percent ownership in the company.

At the same time, Seaborg formed a separate advisory board, based at the DOE's Lawrence Berkeley Laboratory (Seaborg's office), to oppose an organization formed at the University of California at Irvine called S.A.F.E. (System for Aneutronic Fusion Energy). Thrust into APC's management were chemist Albert Ghiorso, 82, Seaborg's assistant from Berkeley, named Chief Scientist; Hollywood actor Harry Hamlin (L.A. Law), named chief science policy maker; and installed as APC's President was no less than the owner of a woman's boutique from Laguna Beach, California.

The Nuclear lobby neglected, however, to advise Seaborg that issuing to one's self free shares without offering them to all shareholders and without a shareholder's meeting is conspiracy and stock fraud. Another detail lost in the shuffle was Maglich's contract: He could only be fired if $5 million were paid to him. Further, using federal premises like the DOE's Lawrence Berkeley Lab in operation of a private company is illegal.

Just one year earlier, speaking about clean fusion in an interview on CNN's "Future Watch," Seaborg had said: "This was all started by Maglich, the man I admire." The same man who invented plutonium for the Manhattan Project and Chaired the Atomic Energy Commission under three presidents was not "Darth Vader" turned to the light. Rather, he remained "Darth Vader" while he used his front as a transformed man to protect what he had always believed in: War. But that might not have been all he was protecting.

After Speaking in Congress in April, 1992 as Director of The Tesla Foundation with Maglich and many brilliant scientists in support of government funding of aneutronic fusion, I deduced, upon our loss, that this government was either incredibly stupid for rejecting such revolutionary technology or they had already achieved our goals and sequestered the technology somewhere on earth. Because several Nobel Prize winners were in support of Maglich, I could not deduce that the government was rejecting it out of stupidity. I could only deduce the second hypothesis: there was an area of the government that had already achieved these goals and it was being protected from public sight.

More and more as time passed by, I was convinced that the conspiracy was real. But what was on the other side? Is there really a protected and hidden alternative space program that insists on being superior to the public space and energy programs? Was such a program threatened by an energy source that could compete with it? I realized this theory was far-fetched but I had to consider it. The only reason I could consider it is because a certain amount of evidence pointed me towards it: I had seen amazing objects on the NASA video making impossible angular turns and hyper-velocity space travel at speeds far beyond rocketry. Someone was already using nuclear propulsion systems, but who?

After working as an executive for HiEnergy Microdevices as a Defense contractor in 1996-1998, I handled a lot of the company's contracts with the Department of Defense and communications with National Security personnel in the Pentagon. I knew how big contractors did business with the Departments of Defense and Energy. I also learned who they are.
In aerospace, there is Boeing, EG&G and SAIC (Science Applications International Corporation). I decided to search their websites to see what they were working on.

I found a fantastic clue on EG&G's website (www.egginc.com) under its history review section. Starting in 1961, the Atomic Energy Commission, Chaired by Glenn Seaborg, prepared to resume nuclear weapon's testing while EG&G provided technical and management support to the test activities. They were directly involved with the testing and Seaborg. In 1962, MIT scientists shined a laser light on the moon using EG&G xenon flashtubes. In 1963, the Limited Test ban Treaty was signed and underground nuclear weapons testing begins at NTS (Nuclear Test Site).

Now here is what I was looking for: In 1968, at the Nuclear Rocket Development Station in Nevada, operated by EG&G, Phoebus 2A, the most powerful nuclear reactor yet developed for space propulsion, is successfully tested.

Now guess where the largest number of alleged UFO sightings have been filmed in the United States: Area-51 in Nevada, the very place EG&G developed its successful nuclear propulsion systems. If the program for using nuclear energy for propulsion was "successful" back in 1968, we can only hypothesize how far advanced it is today. If it is advanced today, then one may deduct that there truly could be an alternative space program that utilizes nuclear energy and nuclear propulsion systems. Nuclear propulsion systems, as demonstrated earlier, may be capable of the speeds detected on the NASA video.

If this program for using nuclear propulsion systems is as advanced as I hypothesize it might be (1968-2001) today, NASA could be using the space shuttle as a mere puppet show to the public while even NASA photographs advanced propulsion systems spacecraft right outside its own window.

Glenn Seaborg, as Chairman of the AEC in Nevada at the time of these nuclear propulsion system developments by EG&G, would be well aware of, and may have administered secrecy for the alternative space program. Seeing Maglich's energy source as a threat, Seaborg may have planned all along to thwart any progress made by Maglich by making the great effort to contact Maglich and get inside his own company. Seaborg did achieve this goal. He died in 1999. Only he knows his true intent.

In 1969, EG&G companies supplied numerous electronic and mechanical components to NASA's Apollo project for its historic moon landing in July. In 1970, an award was presented to EG&G by Associated Industries of Massachusetts for its research and product contributions to the Apollo manned space program.

Maybe EG&G shared some of its discoveries with NASA's public space program, but not all of it. If they shared all of it, including nuclear propulsion systems, then NASA would have to be running the alleged "Alternative Space Program."

If EG&G was developing actual spacecraft utilizing nuclear energy and propulsions systems upon its success in 1968, by now the evidence would have to surface somewhere. If such systems utilizing nuclear energy were still radioactive (and they must be if they were derived from uranium fission), then wherever such flights occurred, there would have to be a certain amount of radiation present.

I can't even count how many stories of alleged UFO abductions and physical encounters with UFOs I have heard where witnesses were treated for radiation burns.

A woman named Betty Cash, one of three people exposed to radiation during a UFO encounter near Huffman, Texas, on December 29, 1980, died in 1998, in Birmingham, Alabama. After the encounter, Betty Cash was hospitalized and treated for burns and the other injuries.

Betty Cash, along with Vicki Landrum and grandson Colby Landrum, encounter a huge UFO accompanied by military helicopters on a dark road in the East Texas Piney Woods. They were exposed to radiation upon encountering the UFO, which caused severe medical problems such as burns, eye damage, hair loss, diarrhea, and vomiting. Although they and others observed a large number of military helicopters along with the UFO, the U.S. Government refused to acknowledged the event.

Eventually, she developed cancer, which was successfully treated. In November 1998, Mrs. Cash suffered a stroke. On December 29, 1998, during her recovery, an unusual turn of events claimed her life.

Chapter Four
Inter-Dimensional Observations

"The power of accurate observation is commonly called cynicism by those who have not got it" – George Bernard Shaw

I – Freedom of Information Act?

My long awaited answer from Dr. Joseph Nuth, III at NASA regarding my Freedom of Information Act request against him had finally arrived. It was a big envelope with a video inside and a signed letter from Dr. Nuth. It read:

Dear Mr. Sereda;

Enclosed with this letter is my entire file on the matter in question, including the video tape that you so kindly sent to me for my comment. I did not send copies of my email replies to your previous email messages as I infer from the content of this present letter that you retain your own copies of this correspondence. Since I am not at all interested in the speculations of Dr. Lou Frank, and since my own research interests do not involve the data sets upon which those speculations are based, I have no other information on these matters than that enclosed – all of which was sent by you.

Signed,

Dr. Joseph A. Nuth III
Head, Astrochemistry Branch
P.S. Thanks for the great stamps. I had not seen anything like them previously.

I had a great laugh to myself when I received this letter. My FOIA request led to NASA giving me back my own file at NASA. There was nothing else. As far as Dr. Nuth was concerned, he had no other data or video to share with me. At this point I felt grateful how open the agency had been with me. There was so much information in these letters, even more than I had applied to the video, I could make many of my own assumptions based on that information. I thank Dr. Nuth for sharing as much information as he did. At this point, I didn't think he would ever write me again.

I wrote Dr. Nuth telling him that I had a good laugh at myself when I received his letter and my video. I try to keep a sense of humor about my own self. He wrote me back and helped me track down Dr. Louis A. Frank at the University of Iowa, in Iowa City. He is the scientist I should really be talking to because Dr. Frank is the one who was making the observations of the mysterious phenomenon. It wasn't easy to find Dr. Frank. My search would have to go on. In the meantime, I wrote Dr. Nuth again the followig letter:

Dear Dr. Nuth,

I am not looking for someone to agree with me just for "agreements" to be made. I am looking for an answer that is intelligent that both I, and others can understand as a logical explanation. You wrote me, I quote the intelligent comment: "I'd suggest that you count the number of objects between the earth and the shuttle (assume and altitude of ~300 mi.), use to calculate a "space density" for these objects. Multiply this space density by the mass of the objects to figure the influx of material to the surface of the Earth. Or, use this density to figure the time for the shuttle or an average satellite to be struck by one of these objects. Not only is the mass flux much too high to ignore, but no satellite has a chance in surviving days, let alone years if these were actually meteors."

While Dr. Nuth was arguing with me on one side of reasoning (NASA), he was telling me the truth hidden in scientific data on the other side of reasoning. Essentially, he was admitting to me that what ever these objects that Dr. Louis A. Frank had discovered, there were too many of them visiting Earth each year to be meteors or "small comets" because they would inevitably destroy every satellite in orbit around the planet if they were, and maybe impact with Earth causing further damage. They haven't done that so he deduces that they could not actually be meteors. They were then a great mystery. NASA was admitting that this *something* that Dr. Frank had discovered was real, the two scientists just didn't agree with one another as to what they are.

I would have to reach Dr. Louis A. Frank and get more information from him to see if there were any similarities to the objects in the NASA videotape to his discovery because Dr. Nuth wouldn't admit that. Again, finding Dr. Frank, even with Dr. Nuth's help, was not easy. I had to keep trying.

Dr. Nuth replied to my last letter in a sixth, very long letter to me on February 22, 1999, giving me more data to make my own assumptions than he ever has. Instead of ending our debate, he opened an infinite number of possibilities:

Dear Mr. Sereda,

First a few facts: most meteors travel in prograde orbits near the ecliptic plane (this is up to + or − 23 degrees from the equator, depending on the season). This means that any meteors that you see from outside earth should travel roughly parallel paths; most meteors have velocities greater than 20 km/s − some travel slower, most travel faster − so the amount of time they would appear on video tape would be very brief and those entering the atmosphere would flare, then fade very rapidly unless they were reasonably massive (~kg); no uncontrolled object violates the laws of physics − we may not know why an object does something, but our ignorance does not mean that "laws" were broken, only that we do not have all the facts. This is especially true for the most basic laws of classical dynamics that have stood for centuries of testing − only failing at relativistic velocities; finally, the cameras in the payload bay are optimized to look at things near the shuttle and have fairly good near-field focus. In addition, the shuttle is an extremely "dirty" environment. There are continuous leaks (at a very low level) from all the manned areas, sporadic outgassing from equipment as well as vented gas from specific experimental activities. All this motion stirs up the "dust bunnies" not fully cleaned out from the various nooks and crannies of the shuttle.

Now for a bit of clarification: I said that there are some places on the tape where the dust balls seemed to disappear, and others appeared seemingly from nowhere. This occurs because some orientations of the shuttle throw shadows at the corners of the camera's field of view. The objects entering or exiting these shadows appear and disappear before reaching the edge of the field of view. This tells me that the objects are within the shuttle bay and not between the earth and the shuttle. I also said that the objects were floating. This is based on the many hours of flight experience I have on the KC-135 (NASA's vomit Comet), the aircraft that flies parabolic trajectories to simulate zero gravity. Objects – and especially dirt and dust – floating in the cargo bay of the KC-135 looked and behaved exactly like the objects on your tape. Finally, the reason I suggest for the seemingly impossible turns that a few objects take is that such particles are caught in bursts of gas released by out-gassing, operating equipment or minor leaks. If these objects are as small and light as I suspect, they are extremely easy to move.

In reply to your question on the astronauts comment concerning a possible meteor – I note that there was no comment concerning a host of objects, just one. I also note that, since the astronauts were not in the field of view of the camera, we can not know where they were looking at the time of the comment and can not associate an object from the video with the remark. There are many meteors entering the atmosphere each and every day and several have been filmed. None of these float and are gone very quickly.

Finally, you must realize that scientists are some of the most skeptical and conservative individuals in existence. As a first approximation we disbelieve everything and will only use knowledge that we have not yet been able to disprove. Data and theories that have been tested for many centuries are probably wrong – but only in very subtle ways under normal circumstances. If there is a simple explanation for an observation that defies some of these time-tested theories we usually opt to go with the simple explanation unless there is a strong reason to think otherwise. As a second working hypothesis, we seldom believe that we are either much smarter or more perceptive than anyone else except on very rare cases. Therefore, if there is an observational phenomenon that often occurs in particular set of circumstances, and no one has yet tagged it as a very unusual or remarkable happening, most scientists viewing the occurrence will not automatically assume that the explanation must be at the frontiers of knowledge (because our experience has been that most unusual observations have very mundane explanations). If the phenomenon is interesting enough to deserve an investigation, then our preference would be for controlled experiments that closely duplicate the circumstances of the original observation and test our working hypothesis until they are either verified or falsified. A second line of investigation would be to obtain more evidence of the original sightings (e.g. additional shuttle camera tapes – there are at least 4 mounted in the bay) to see if the same objects were seen on these. If these objects were large, then the same object should appear on two or more cameras and these can be used to triangulate the distance from the shuttle to the object. If there are no objects that appear simultaneously on two or more cameras, then one must conclude that the objects seen are in the near-fields of the individual cameras – and the dust bunny hypothesis gets stronger.

I would ask that you apply this line of reasoning and the tests proposed in my last email and above to the evidence in hand to see which more consistently explains the observations.

Joe Nuth

The first point Dr. Nuth reiterates can easily be disproved: "I also said that the objects were floating. This is based on the many hours of flight experience I have on the KC-135 (NASA's vomit Comet), the aircraft that flies parabolic trajectories to simulate zero gravity. Objects – and especially dirt and dust – floating in the cargo bay of the KC-135 looked and behaved exactly like the objects on your tape."

As I pointed out earlier, with CCD digital video cameras, such as NASA was using, the depth of field is so phenomenal, near-field objects do not appear out of focus and fuzzy at all. Rather, they appear with all the detail and good visibility required to see exactly what they are.

Once the CCD Video camera is in focus on a distant object such as the Earth 300 miles away, then everything is in focus including near-field objects. I held a set of keys 4 inches in front of the video camera while focused on a tree 200 feet away. Both remain in perfect focus. Even Dr. Nuth admitted to the good depth of field of the NASA Video cameras. This means that if an object 4 inches from the camera is in focus simultaneous to the distant object being in focus, there can be no possible appearances of "Airy Discs" around pieces of junk or debris. So out-of-focus blobs or optical illusions like you are supposing cannot occur. The video cam I used is certainly not as good as the ones used on the shuttle.

Also, the only time I could produce "Airy Discs" in my video camera tests was when I threw the whole camera out of focus. When this happens, everything is a blur and no distinctions can be made about anything. We know from the STS-75 tether incident that Claude Nicolier said, "I'm trying to adjust the focus, but I can't get any better than that." The camera is too easy to focus. These hi-tech video cameras can be focused on distant objects by a child they are so easy to use. We know he had the cam in focus and that means everything, including near-field objects would also be in focus so no fuzzy orbs could appear. Nothing in between could be out of focus, as the law of depth of field demonstrates.

The second point Dr. Nuth makes about the "Hubble Repair Sequence" on the tape is completely distorted, "In reply to your question on the astronauts comment concerning a possible meteor – I note that there was no comment concerning a host of objects, just one. I also note that, since the astronauts were not in the field of view of the camera, we can not know where they were looking at the time of the comment and can not associate an object from the video with the remark."

First of all, the astronauts dialogs on the video never refers to the object as a "possible meteor," rather, "You have an object right out there in front of you Mark. Are you looking out there?" Mark's reply is, "I don't see what you are talking about." The answer is, "It's about your Ten O, Clock, Eleven, O, Clock going away. Don't worry about it."

Dr. Nuth said that the "astronauts were not in the field of view of the camera" and they are clearly in view while they are commenting about this object. Dr. Nuth also says that, "we cannot know where they were looking at the time of the comment and can not associate an object from the video with the remark." When the astronaut tells Mark, "It's about your Ten O, Clock, Eleven O, Clock going away, don't worry about it," we can clearly look to that position and see the flashing light passing far away from them.

The fact that the astronauts have a "Don't worry about it" attitude suggests that they have either been briefed to expect such encounters and regard them as harmless, or that they have also seen them numerous times before and regard them as no threat.

The most honest and constructive thing Dr. Nuth had to say in this letter was this: "If the phenomenon is interesting enough to deserve an investigation, then our preference would be for controlled experiments that closely duplicate the circumstances of the original observation and test our working hypothesis until they are either verified or falsified. A second line of investigation would be to obtain more evidence of the original sightings (e.g. additional shuttle camera tapes – there are at least 4 mounted in the bay) to see if the same objects were seen on these. If these objects were large, then the same object should appear on two or more cameras and these can be used to triangulate the distance from the shuttle to the object. If there are no objects that appear simultaneously on two or more cameras, then one must conclude that the objects seen are in the near-fields of the individual cameras – and the dust bunny hypothesis gets stronger."

The NASA video footage I was about to see for the first time would provide our group with the evidence to put NASA in a "Check-Mate" position. It was the "Holy Grail" that I was looking for in this investigation.

II - MEETING MARTYN STUBBS

I had mailed Martyn Stubbs copies of all the e-mail letters I had received from Dr. Joseph Nuth, III at NASA up to this time. He was really excited about the investigation. I had never seen the face of the man I had been talking on the phone with for 2 years now.

I arrived In Vancouver, B.C. Canada in the summer of 1999. I went to meet Martyn Stubbs with my photographer friend Mike Boyle. Mike had worked diligently for 4 years to put this meeting together. Martyn lived somewhere on an Island away from civilization. He had retired from working at the CABLE TV station, where he recorded all of the NASA broadcasts via satellite, due to developing a brain tumor.

Conspiracy theories started flying in my head. Martyn Stubbs was a former Director of MUFON (Mutual UFO Network). He didn't share this information with them entirely because he didn't think they were intelligent enough to handle the investigation.

While we were on the ferryboat ride to Martyn's island, Mike and I joked about how the CIA and National Security agencies must have tapped Martyn's telephones and sent harmful radio frequencies through his ears, into his brain to give him a brain tumor just because he was a threat to NASA and the secret government. We were next. We were joking but we were also not joking. Why do so many UFO researchers die of cancer, brain tumors and heart attacks? The humorous theories started to work their way feverishly into my brain. I always wanted to meet the alleged "Men in Black," and maybe the only way to find out if they are real is to get deeper involved into a project like this. Expose the government's knowledge of UFOs and meet these guys in person, shake their hands and get abducted to their secret base in Washington, D.C., "not."

We got off the ferryboat and Martyn was waiting for us in a truck. He was a poor, slovenly dressed man with frizzy long hair like Albert Einstein's after the first nuclear test on July 5, 1945. People who border on genius rarely spend time for outer appearances unless they are in high profile meetings. His eyes were that of a man who had a sense of humor and a man who bordered on genius. He looked like he had seen more than I could imagine. Even though he had a brain tumor, he functioned very well.

We greeted each other and Mike and I followed Martyn trailing in my car behind. We were about to see NASA video that far surpassed anything we had seen to date. Mike was right. Martyn had hid his best footage from us for 4 years.

We got to Martyn's very nice country home. His sundeck had a fabulous view of the ocean and forested island. I could see a stack of nearly 100 NASA videos that were part of his library. I had only seen a one-hour tape.

Martyn, Mike and myself all had a strong spiritual background. That became our foundation for trust in each other. While most religions in the world were at war with each other, we were not. We all had different religious beliefs and experiences but we saw each other eye-to-eye. Martyn trusted me enough to give me an apple before he showed Mike and I the forbidden fruits of NASA's 1990s space shuttle missions.

III - STS-75 THE TETHER INCIDENT

Before Martyn showed us the forbidden NASA video, he presented me with a copy of an article about a strange event that happened during NASA's STS-75 mission entitled, "Satellite Signals a Puzzle," which ran in The United Press International in February, 1996. It reads as follows:

CAPE CANAVERAL, Fla. – NASA found a few surprises when it restored contact with a wayward spacecraft, officials said yesterday.

The $100-million-US Italian atmospheric probe inadvertently became a free-flyer Sunday night when its 20.7 kilometer (12 miles) tether to the shuttle Columbia snapped.

U.S. National Aeronautics and Space Administration engineers were able to contact the satellite Monday and turn on its science instruments, designed to collect information on Earth's electromagnetic fields and electrically charged particles in the atmosphere.

First radio signals from the satellite caused engineers some surprise: The configuration of several systems had changed from when NASA lost contact with the craft on Sunday.

For example, the spacecraft's nitrogen fuel tank was empty and its steering-thruster valves were opened. In addition, a gyroscope that had been left on was powered off, while two other gyroscopes remained on.

"There has been an event on the satellite that we do not understand yet," astronaut David Wolf told the Columbia crew.

What kind of a force could have taken control of the satellite (spacecraft) and manipulated all of its control systems without the astronaut's knowing? In the Hollywood movie "2001 A Space Odyssey" by the legendary science fiction write "Arthur C. Clark," the fictional Hal 9000 computer takes over the controls of the space craft on its way to Jupiter and kills the entire crew. The computer malfunctioned to save the mission. All of the controls were taken over by a computer.

If "David Wolf" tells the space shuttle Columbia crew, "there has been an event on the satellite that we do not understand yet," then it couldn't be an obvious possible computer malfunction. Obviously the nitrogen fuel tank that was emptied was not controllable by computer. How then did the phenomenon occur?

Martyn Stubbs had a wicked smile on his face because he knew the answer. He played the STS-75 "Tether Incident" on his large-screen television. It was astounding. Mike and I watched in as much amazement, and more, than my friend Tommy and I did when we first saw a real UFO in Berkeley, California in 1968.

The Shuttle Columbia was flying over the west coast of northern Africa, the home of Earth's most ancient civilizations and the Great pyramids of ancient Egypt.

The shuttle Columbia crew was filming the event with its familiar low-light level black and white cameras. We were looking at a satellite (just a dot) attached to a 12-mile long conductor cable called a tether. The tether formerly connected between the shuttle and the satellite. It was used as a new experiment to conduct electricity while the tether passed through the Earth's electrically charged ionosphere. According to NASA reports, the tether produced more electricity than had been calculated and the tether cable could not handle the amounts of electricity produced. This may have been what caused the tether to snap and break off from the shuttle.

As the NASA commentators told us the shuttle was 77 nautical miles away from the tether, the satellite and tether appeared just as a long cigar shape (the 12-mile long tether) with a dot at the end (the satellite). Suddenly these brightly glowing objects started to arrive very quickly and gather around the tethered satellite. Soon, there was about five of them.
The NASA commentator told us that the planet Venus was one of the objects we were seeing but then the alleged planet started to move and the cameras jolted away.

When the cameras panned back to the tethered satellite, a swarm of over fifty of these amazing objects started to gather from the far reaches of the space above the earth. It was the most amazing sight I had ever seen on film. We were told the distance between the shuttle Columbia and the tethered satellite was over 77 nautical miles. The cameras zoomed in to get a closer look at these mysterious objects to reveal "The Holy Grail."

From a distance, the objects appeared the same as the other anomalies on the NASA videotape. But now we were getting the first close-up view. The objects were classic UFO disc-shaped objects. There were so many of them. They had obvious square shaped portals at the edge of their circular appearance. There was a dot in the center of each one. The portals appeared to be morphing as the crafts moved: what a strange ability.

The "Holy Grail" of evidence was the very obvious fact that these objects were clearly passing behind the satellite and tether eliminating Dr. Nuth's last hypothesis that in the previous tape he had seen, "then one must conclude that the objects seen are in the near-fields of the individual cameras – and the dust bunny hypothesis gets stronger."

Because the tethered satellite was clearly stated to be 77-100 nautical miles away from the shuttle Columbia, and our mysterious objects were passing behind the tethered satellite, they could not be debris, "dust bunnies" or anything near the shuttle environment.

Astoundingly, because the tether was 12 miles in length, we now eliminated Dr. Nuth's sophisticated trigonometry to calculate distance from the shuttle to the object and then the object's size, "If these objects were large, then the same object should appear on two or more cameras and these can be used to triangulate the distance from the shuttle to the object."

As the mysterious disc shaped objects passed behind the tethered satellite, we could measure their minimum sizes against the 12-mile long tether. What a perfect measuring rod. The sizes we would calculate would be minimum sizes because if they were within ten yards behind the tether, our sizes would be accurate, but if they were far behind the tether, then their sizes would increase. If one holds a finger up to the sun and tries to measure the sun's size against their finger as the sun passes behind their finger, the sun would appear to be much smaller than it really is because it is so very far behind the finger.

Utilizing such simple physics, I calculated the sizes of the two largest objects as they passed behind the tether. They measured an astounding and minimum diameter of 2-3 miles. This makes these alleged (at this point) UFOs the largest ever caught on video. Because this was government (NASA) video, it was proof of government knowledge of such amazing phenomena. One can only imagine what it was like for the astronauts to witness an "Independence Day" level event like this as it really happened.

What was it like to see this for the Columbia crew as they had seen it live? The STS-75 Crew consisted of two European Space Agency astronauts, Claude Nicollier (who manned the video camera and filmed this event) and Maurizio Cheli, one from the Italian Space Agency, Umberto Guidoni, and four from NASA, Andrew Allen, Scott J.

Horowitz, Franklin Chang Diaz (physicist who comments live during this event), and Jeffrey Hoffman. All of these men walked on Earth knowing that a remarkable event took place on the STS-75 mission in February of 1996, but they weren't going to the press with this story. Since 1996, nowhere in the UFO movement did this NASA video footage surface.

Martyn enjoyed the looks on Mike Boyle and my face more than watching the tether. We were flabbergasted. Some of the UFOs seemed to be pulsing with waves of energy. You could actually see these waves on the video. It may have been their propulsion system.

NASA Control in Huntsville, Alabama communicated with the shuttle Columbia crew live saying, "We see a long line, a couple of star-like things and a lot of things swimming in the foreground. Can you describe what you are seeing?" They had obviously seen the same picture. How could anyone miss the swarm of UFOs? The answer was the most retarded theory anyone could possibly come up with and it comes from an astronaut and nuclear physicist named Franklin Chang-Diaz: "The long line is the tether. There's a lot of stray light and things getting washed out and…Claude is trying to adjust the camera….."

How does light go astray? Light is a constant. It cannot go astray. It follows the natural laws of physics. In space, because there is no moisture in a vacuum, light distortions would be impossible or minor at the very most. No light distortion could cause a full apparition as what NASA was alleging to what we were seeing. These objects had clear size, shape and architecture. This was no light distortion or "stray light," effect.

I became more and more appalled at how NASA's cover-ups and lies were completely amateur. They weren't even good covers. Only a grade-four astronomy student in elementary school would believe what they were saying.

The shuttle camera now zoomed back away from the tethered satellite, now 100 nautical miles away, and we could see that the swarm of these UFOs was even larger than fifty. The objects were so astounding in their movement (they moved so freely) that one might suggest that they were "living beings" of enormous size flying through outer space.

Maybe these were not spacecraft, but the extraterrestrial beings themselves. After all, why would an extraterrestrial have to move and behave just like a human to be deemed a living being?

Mike Boyle made an amazing observation that "None of them seem to collide with one another," which would be expected if the UFOs were some form of space particles drifting about. They never hit one another. This was truly amazing.

If NASA would propose that the objects were natural and unintelligent particles again, they would have to follow Galileo's law of gravity: all bodies, regardless of weight, size, density or shape, fall through a void in gravity at the same speed. In the sixteenth century, Galileo dropped metal balls of different weights off of the "Leaning Tower if Pizza" to discover that, regardless on the different weights, they all fell at exactly the same rate of seed and landed on the ground at the same time. He tested and re-tested this until it became a primary law of physics. This is because gravity is a constant.

These objects were clearly breaking Galileo's and Newton's law of gravity because they were all moving through the same space at completely different rates of velocity: some at total zero (just hovering), some (timed against the length of 12 miles of tether per second) 1,000 mph and some 35,000 mph. Just the fact that they broke a most fundamental law of physics proved that they were free of the effects of earth's gravity and had internal energy and propulsion: something no natural object could have.

The Command Center radio control operator is seeing the picture live also. He says to the Columbia crew, "The tether seems to resemble a much wider strand than we'd expect." No one answered him. The tether was just a relatively thin conductor cable made of kevlar. From 100 nautical miles, it should barely be visible. It must have become ionized like a neon tube somehow.

Before I would consider sending this incredible piece of NASA video to Dr. Nuth, I wanted to study everything I could about the tether experiment to see if NASA had a plausible explanation. As Dr. Nuth had also said, "most scientists viewing the occurrence will not automatically assume that the explanation must be at the frontiers of knowledge because our experience has been that most unusual observations have very mundane explanations."

NASA knew that this event was broadcast to the world live. Someone out there had to have seen it. Whether anyone had videotaped it, they didn't know. While Dr. Franklin Chang-Diaz's ludicrous statements on the video about, "stray light" causing the alleged apparitions wouldn't hold under scientific scrutiny, NASA had to come up with a more elaborate theory. They had plenty of time to do that because no one was coming forward to question the event, probably because no one was watching who had taped it except Martyn Stubbs. Martyn didn't know when events like this would happen. That is why he recorded missions from beginning to end.

I decided to research the communications systems on the space shuttle because it seemed that there had to be more serious communications about these alleged UFOs. My theory was that those communications that revealed the real truth as to what the astronauts were seeing would not be broadcast to the public. The public would get the watered down lies that Franklin Chang Diaz was telling us live, "There's a lot of stray light and things are getting washed out. There's some debris kind of flying with us and it's getting illuminated by the sun at such low angles."

While the public was supposed to accept this obvious lie, those who had a sense of scientific understanding would not accept it. The alleged UFOs were passing behind a satellite that was 77-100 nautical miles away from the cameras. This is absolute confirmation that these objects were not debris floating near the shuttle. The public was lied to by NASA.

In the NASA space shuttle manual section on the "Payload Communication System," we find the technology that the shuttle uses to communicate back to Earth. Communications between NASA, the Department of Defense and payloads (satellites, etc.) are made on several different radio frequencies as the manual reveals:

Communication with an attached payload takes place through the payload patch panel at the crew compartment flight deck aft station, which is connected to external equipment with internal systems. From this panel, the attached payload telemetry can take different paths. All standard command and telemetry signals are processed on board. Non-standard signals are sent to the ground through Ku-band. This method of transmission, referred to as bent-pipe telemetry, means that no onboard signal processing occurs before the telemetry is sent to the Ku-band system. Payload telemetry can go directly to the S-band, FM or Ku-band systems for transmission to the ground, payload data interleaver to be interleaved with other payload data in a selected format called the decommutator format load. The systems also processes commands and tracks the status of various payload-related controls and displays.

Detached payloads (satellites, etc.) communicate with the orbiter (shuttle) on an RF signal through the payload antenna by the payload interrogator. The main frequency carrier of the detached payload telemetry is demodulated by the PI. The telemetry is sent directly to the Ku-band systems for transmission to the ground (bent-pipe telemetry) or to the payload signal processors. The PSP demodulates the subcarrier from the telemetry and sends the telemetry to the payload data interleaver to be interleaved with other payload data. Attached payload commands are routed to the PSP and then to the payload patch panel, which is also referred to as the payload station distribution panel. Detached payload commands are routed to the PSP and then to the PI for transmission through the payload antenna.

The communication interface unit replaces the PSPS during DOD (Department of Defense) missions and uses space-ground-link-system-compatible payloads and ground stations to provide communication security.

This last section reveals that Department of Defense has a secure communications line with the space shuttle. When we consider that space shuttle encounters with UFOs would be a National Security issue, such communications would flow directly through to NASA and the DOD, obviating the public out of the truth as to what those communications would have been. The manual continues:

The CIU interfaces indirectly with the payload data interleaver through the patch panel because the CIU is treated as an attached payload accessed through a patch panel input of the payload data interleaver. The payload signal processor is hard-wired directly to the payload data interleaver.

The S-band payload antenna is located on the top of the outer skin of the orbiter's forward fuselage, just aft of the upper hemispherical antenna. The payload antenna is covered with reusable thermal protection system. This antenna is used as the radiating element for S-band transmission and reception to and from the orbiter to detach payloads through the forward link and return link.

The basic elements in the payload communication system are the payload interrogator, payload signal processor, communication interface unit, payload data interleaver, pulse code modulation master unit, payload patch panel, payload recorder and payload MDMs 1 and 2. These elements are in the forward avionics bay and are controlled by switches on panels A1 and L10. The payload interrogator is a transmitter/receiver unit that provides full duplex RF communications between the orbiter and a detached payload. It transmits commands to and receives telemetry from NASA or DOD-compatible payloads through the payload antenna.

Communication problems involving antenna position relative to payload position are not evident while the payload is within a half mile of the orbiter. However, to maintain good communication with the orbiter from distances of several miles, the payload must be within an 80degree beam-width (with reference to minus Z axis) of the orbiter's PI antenna. The boundary of the 80-degree beam-width is the 3-decibel point (or half-power point), which must be considered during communication with deployed payloads. This constraint is normally satisfied by the payload and retrieval process.

The payload interrogator receiver automatically acquires and tracks an unmodulated or modulated RF signal. PI telemetry is available through the unmodulated or modulated RF signal. PI telemetry is available through the operational instrumentation MDM to verify signal strength and frequency lock.

When the payload outputs a data rate that is not compatible with the payload signal processor or communication interface unit, all data received by the PI is throughput (bent-pipe) directly to the K-band signal processor through a dedicated channel that operates independently of, but parallel to, the NASA and DOD channels. Standard payload telemetry is sent to the PSP for processing before being routed to the payload data interleaver.

The payload signal processor is the command interface between the ground or flight crew and five attached/detached payload services. It is also a detached payload telemetry interface to the payload data interleaver.

The communication interface unit is used in place of the PSP whenever an SGLS-compatible payload is flown. This provides a command and telemetry path between the orbiter guidance, navigation and control GPC and an SGLS-compatible payload or between the flight crew and an SGLS-compatible payload. The CIU passes commands and telemetry to either attached or detached payloads.

The NASA mission configuration, the payload patch panel interfaces attached payloads to the PDI. Attached payloads are wired to specific input channels in the PPP during pre-launch activities. When the PDI is reconfigured by the flight crew, programming procedures include assigning inputs from the PPP to the desired decommutator.

The DOD configuration, the PPP is the command and telemetry interface between the CIU and attached payloads as well as the telemetry interface for detached payloads from the CIU to the PDI.

The payload data interleaver allows the payload communication system to interface with the rest of the orbiter communication system and computers. It receives up to six different inputs from attached or detached payloads and one test input. For missions using the PSP, a maximum of five attached payloads can be accommodated on inputs 1 through 5. Input 6 is reserved for detached payload commands and telemetry using the RF link though PSP. For missions using the CIU, all data, attached or detached, are routed through input 5. The PDI routes four of the six available inputs to the PCMMU for downlink to the SM GPC for display purposes.

NASA's website revealed more information about the tether than I could read without advertising the "tether incident" at all. Here is what I found:

On flight day 3, the crew will begin deployment by raising a 40-foot (12-meter) deployment boom that elevates the satellite and its support structure to this height. Once released, the satellite will climb upward from the orbiter and away from Earth, aided by gravitational force and the use of its onboard thrusters, to attain a distance of 12.4 miles (20.7 kilometers) over a 5-1/2 hour period. The crew will control the satellite and deployer system from the aft flight deck.

The attached tether, with a diameter of 0.1 inches (2.5 millimeters) is made of Nomex and Kevlar. This super-strong and thin strand, also contains a tin-coated, insulated copper wire bundle that makes it electrically conductive.

As the tether passes through the electromagnetic fields of the Earth's atmosphere, an electrical charge is expected to build up between the satellite and the orbiter through an electrodynamic process. Electrons from the ionosphere will be collected at the satellite and will travel down the tether orbiter. The Deployer Core Equipment (DCORE) instrument in the payload bay will control this flow of electrical current in the tether with two electron generator assemblies. The Shuttle Electrodynamic Tether Systems (SETS) will provide measurements of the tether voltage and current and generate an electron beam in support of science investigations. The Shuttle Potential and Return Electron Experiment (SPREE) will measure ion and electron distribution and determine the orbiter electrical potential. Other investigations will study the effects of the deployed tether and satellite on the space environment.

Approximately 27 hours after deployment, the crew will activate the 5-horsepower electric motor that will rewind the tether and draw the satellite back to the top of the satellite support structure in the payload bay. The retrieval will be conducted in two phases over a period of 18 hours.

That was how NASA foresaw this mission before it had happened. Obviously, when the tether broke on Sunday, February 25 at 7:30 PM, the experiment did not go as intended. Something went terribly wrong.
To find out what went wrong, we would have to learn more about what this tether was supposed to be doing from its manufacture:

An electrodynamic tether is essentially a long conducting wire extended from a spacecraft. The gravity gradient field (also known as the "tidal force") will tend to orient the tether in a vertical position. If the tether is orbiting around the Earth, it will be crossing the Earth's magnetic field lines at orbital velocity (7-8 km/s). The motion of the conductor across the magnetic field induces a voltage along the length of the tether. This voltage can be up to several hundred volts per kilometer.

In an "electrodynamic tether drag" system, such as the Terminator Tether, the tether can be used to reduce the orbit of the spacecraft to which it is attached. If the system has a means for collecting electrons from the ionospheric plasma at one end of the tether and expelling them back into the plasma at the other end of the tether, the voltage can drive a current along the tether. This current will, in turn, interact with the Earth's magnetic field to cause a Lorentz JXB force which will oppose the motion of the tether and whatever it is attached to. This "electrodynamic drag force" will decrease the orbit of the tether and its host spacecraft. Essentially, the tether converts the orbital energy of the host spacecraft into electrical power, which is dissipated as ohmic heating in the tether.

In an "electrodynamic propulsion" system, the tether can be used to boost the orbit of the spacecraft. If a power supply is added to the tether system and used to drive current in the direction opposite to that which it normally wants to flow, the tether can "push" against the Earth's magnetic field to raise the spacecraft's orbit. The major advantage of this technique compared to other space propulsion systems is that it doesn't require propellant. It uses the Earth's magnetic field as its "reaction mass." By eliminating the need to launch large amounts of propellant into orbit, electrodynamic tethers can greatly reduce the cost of in-space propulsion.

For example, the International Space Station (ISS) will experience a small but constant aerodynamic drag force as it moves through the thin upper reaches of the Earth's atmosphere. This drag force will cause the station's orbit to decay. If nothing were done to counteract this, the station would fall out of orbit within several months. NASA currently plans to launch several large rockets every year to carry fuel up to the station so that it can reboost its orbit. These launches, however, will be very costly.

Tethers Unlimited, Inc. has helped NASA to explore the potential for using electrodynamic tether propulsion to maintain the orbit of ISS. By using excess power generated by the ISS's solar panels to drive current through a conductor tether, a tether reboost system could counteract the drag forces or even raise the station's orbit. NASA and TUI's studies revealed that such a tether reboost system could reduce or eliminate the need for dedicated launches for reboost propellant, potentially saving u to $2 billion over the first ten years of the station's operation.

Electrodynamic tethers may also provide an economical means of electrical power in orbit. Essentially, the tether can be used to convert some of the spacecraft's orbital energy into electrical power. However, since converting the orbital energy into electrical power will lower the orbit of the spacecraft (there's no such thing as free lunch), this technique is probably only useful for providing brief, high-power energy bursts to brief experiments.

Essentially, the tether was a large conductor cable utilizing the natural electricity as it passed through the charged ionosphere above the earth. The natural electricity in the ionosphere was acting upon the tether and flowing through it to give extra energy to the shuttle or future space station. It was a great idea and experiment. The experiment did not go as planned.

So far, the thoughts that came up in our investigation group (Martyn Stubbs, Mike Boyle and myself) were that perhaps the energy produced in the tether radiated out into space like radio signals and attracted these mysterious UFOs. Perhaps they sensed the energy radiating from the tether like a radio tower and all came to see what was causing the signals. It was just a theory, but we had to learn more. I went to NASA's website and keyword searched "tether." I came upon many files that required access codes before one could enter. There was no way to get into those files. I could, however, get into brief files about the tether incident.

The brief files mentioned that the tether produced far more electricity than scientists and engineers had previously calculated. The excess energy may have caused the tether cable to overheat (like a toaster wire) and become brittle and break.

The reports said that they were amazed at how potentially dangerous the incident could have been if the tether had broken in any other place: it could have snapped against the shuttle with such force, the crew and shuttle could have been destroyed. Why did it break in such a place to eliminate the danger? No one could answer it. The report was also not definite about the reasons for breakage. Why were the other reports classified?

Finally I found an open report that had NASA's alleged answers to the phenomenon. This report was made long after the mission was completed, giving NASA time to have explanations. After studying them, I could see that they spent a great deal of time preparing their theories. There were holes all over them, but holes that amateurs would miss. This was the best lie I had ever seen NASA come up with. From the NASA, STS-75 Day 3, Saturday, February 24, 1996, STS-75 MCC Status Report # 04 Highlights, the following are excerpts:

> Once deployed, the tethered satellite will slowly fly away from Columbia, eventually reaching a distance of 12 miles (20 kilometers). Communications and commanding of the satellite itself during deploy and retrieve is done by a radio link to the

Space Shuttle by ground commands from NASA's Marshall Spaceflight Center in Huntsville, which has overall program management for the TSS project.

Meanwhile, Nicollier took video of Earth's horizon using the Tether Optical Phenomena (TOP) equipment. This experiment, conducted by Stephen Mende of Lockheed Martin, involves the use of a camera system with image intensifiers and special filters and will provide visual data that will allow scientists to answer a variety of questions concerning tether motions and optical effects generated during the Tethered Satellite's deployment. In particular, this experiment will examine the high voltage sheath of electrically charged or "ionized" gas that will surround the satellite as it flies through the Earth's ionosphere.

During some nighttime orbital passes, crew members worked with the Tether Optical Phenomena Experiment (TOP), which gave a stunning view of atmospheric air glow and auroras over the South Pole as viewed from the flight deck's overhead window. This is the window through which the crew later will watch the deployed satellite. TOP science team members viewed live video images and sent voice commands to vary the filters and exposure setting for better viewing.

The heart of the TOP instrument is a hand-held low-light video camera with special filters whose primary purpose on TSS is to observe luminescence produced by electron beams and interaction of the electrically charged satellite with the local charged-particle and neutral atmosphere. The TOP has many advantages over similar photographic recordings made on previous flights because it allows real-time observations of the images seen by the orbiter crew.

The Hand-Held Low-Light Video Camera

I needed to investigate the kinds of video cameras NASA was using to see if they could peer into the invisible ultraviolet light spectrum because that is the spectrum of light where high-energy UFOs should be vibrating, in theory. It was also the same spectrum where Dr. Nuth at NASA told me that the observed "SOMETHING" was spotted. The lower light spectrums rarely revealed anything of interest.

NASA had a variety of calls out to defense contractors looking for special video cameras that are capable of seeing into the infrared spectrum, the ultraviolet spectrum, the x-ray spectrum and even the gamma ray spectrum. I was amazed to see how deeply NASA wanted to look into all of these high-energy spectra of energy. Of course they knew that the search for extraterrestrial intelligence would require the ability to observe high energy dimensions of light that were invisible to the human eye.

NASA's Jet Propulsion Laboratories (JPL) in Pasadena, California had developed "a highly sensitive infrared video camera with numerous applications." JPL has been researching infrared photodetectors for the past five years under contract to NASA's Office of Space Access and Technology. But the infrared region was of little interest to me.

NASA had also had contractors retrofit video cameras into "Image Intensified CCD Cameras" that were more sensitive to high frequencies of light. But my real discovery came when I found that a company called Advanced Photonix in Camarillo, California that manufactured special photodiodes. Their technology was originally funded by the Department of Defense for laser receivers and missile detectors. It lead to applications to other agencies as well, including the U.S. Department of Energy, NASA, and the Defense Advanced Research Projects Agency.

The special photodiodes developed by Advanced Photonix are the first solid-state devices to offer sufficient gain, low enough background noise, and adequate active areas to replace photomultiplier tubes in numerous applications. They bring the same qualities of ruggedness, small size, and low cost to low-level light detection that charged-coupled device cameras have brought to video camcorders. They span the near ultraviolet, visible and near infrared spectra of light and are sensitive to charged particles and ionizing radiation. When coupled with scintillation counters, they also detect x-rays and gamma rays.

These video cameras could see into the near ultraviolet range and even into x-rays and gamma rays. This was astounding evidence that the NASA video cameras were not ordinary camcorders. The images we were seeing were truly advanced images peering into the

invisible ultraviolet and possibly x-ray and gamma ray spectrum of light energy.

While video cameras alone are not the only source of recording these missions, good cameras with real film for sharper and clearer images are. My partner Mike Boyle researched Kodak for special films that can be used to enhance the quality of photographing into the invisible spectrum of light. Kodak does make such films. They manufacture everything from electron imaging films to "spectroscopic films useful for applications in scientific and technical photography, including stellar astrophotography, planetary photography, spectrography, holography and other films."

Clearly, cameras and special films could see into the invisible range of light energy better than video cameras, but NASA would use video cameras for their live downlinks to Earth. While what we were seeing on the NASA video was stunning, the high-quality images captured by such cameras and special film must be astounding.

I continued with the report from NASA about the STS-75 "Tether Incident" to see if I could find answers. Everything presented from the report so far was as of Saturday, February 24, 1996, the day before the alleged "Tether UFO incident." It does suggest NASA's new and "contrived" explanations for only a small amount of what we were seeing during the "tether incident."

The first observation is about the "camera system with image intensifiers and special filters," which we now know allowed the camera to see into the Infrared and even ultraviolet invisible ranges of light. This may give the first clue that the objects may not have been visible to the naked eye's of the astronauts. They also may have been using special videotape that helped with sensitivity to light in the UV range. For example, in 1965, EG&G developed "sensitive film under NASA contract to be used by astronauts for lunar photography." One can only imagine what special videotape NASA may have today.

The second observation about the report is: "In particular, this experiment will examine the high voltage sheath of electrically charged or "ionized" gas that will surround the satellite as it flies through the Earth's ionosphere." While this can explain why NASA, Huntsville operator tells the Columbia crew in the video, "The tether seems to resemble a much wider strand than we'd expect" with no answer. The hypothesis is that the ionized gas (like neon gas in a neon light tube) around the satellite and tether may have become ionized by the Earth's ionosphere and began to give the thin tether a "glow," which made it so visible from 100 nautical miles. This theory would not explain the alleged UFOs which come from the far reaches of space and move towards the satellite and tether from great distances in just a few seconds.

The third observation confirms once again the possible reason for the tether and satellite being so visible from such a great distance from the shuttle Columbia, "The heart of the TOP instrument is a hand-held low-light video camera with special filters whose primary purpose on TSS is to observe luminescence produced by electron beams and interaction of the electrically charged satellite with the local charged-particle and neutral atmosphere." This also shows evidence for the footage being in black and white, as previously stated by NASA in "The High-Speed Left Angle Turn Sequence," that "The low-light level black and white cameras provide a much better view of...."

Also in this third observation is "luminescence produced by electron beams and interaction of the electrically charged satellite." This does not mean in any way the subatomic particle like "electrons" can appear to be 2 miles wide. In fact, electrons are invisible to the human eye. Electrons spin around their nucleus (protons) at enormous speeds with no predictable patterns. They are chaotic. In this report, "electron beams" must be energy travelling along the tether." If the tether was producing electricity, and so much that it produced a "short circuit" (the possible cause of the tether break), it may also give reason to suggest why it was so luminous from such a great distance.

The point finally reveals that distorted or "stray light" had very little to do with it. The video camera lens would have been focused on infinity and therefore nothing could have been out of focus. If the camera was out of focus, there would be no appearance of "portals" in the alleged tether UFOs. They would have all just been a blur.

The real irony was, if the astronauts knew what they were doing, and they knew all of this at the time of the experiment, then why didn't they explain this when they were asked by the NASA operator in Huntsville, "We see a long cigar like thing and a lot of objects swimming in the foreground. Can you describe what we're seeing?" The answer from Columbia was not one of knowledge of the phenomena, rather an evasion, "The long light is the tether. There's a lot of stray light. Things are getting washed out."

The next report on NASA's website was from the "tether incident" and would reveal more information and the final "black holes" in NASA's explanations in this report. From the STS-75 Day 4 Highlights, Sunday, February 25, 1996, 6 a.m. CST, STS-75 Payload Status Report # 05:

"At this point, all of the instruments are working fine and returning data," concluded Theory and Modeling in Support of Tether (TMST) Principal Investigator Dr. Adam Drobot in a live interview with WSFA-TV in Montgomery, Alabama. "I think everybody is quite excited that things are going very well." Last night, data collections for the STS-75 mission continued to take advantage of the additional science opportunities afforded by the extra day of predeployment operations as the crew performed science activities in preparation for this afternoon's deployment of the Tethered Satellite System (TSS-1R).

Meanwhile, science teams at the Marshall Space Flight center used the SETS experiment's instruments to give measurements which related to the ionized gas as it interacted with the water cloud. The water molecules in this cloud exchanged electrical charges with the surrounding ionized oxygen and formed a ring shape which could be easily distinguished from the ionized gas background around Columbia. This gave scientists and crew members an idea of how the Shuttle's environment might react to water dumps released while the tethered satellite is deployed.

For a third investigation of the orbiter's ionospheric surroundings, the SETS and SPREE experiments teamed up with the Tether Optical Phenomena (TOP), Research on Orbital Plasma Electrodynamics (ROPE) and research on Electrodynamic Tether effects (RETE) experiments to study the electron beams fired from the SETS experiment's electron gun. Previous measurements indicated that a thin electron beam emitted from the orbiter quickly expands in width to form a cylinder. The effectiveness of these emissions from the orbiter depends on various factors, including the beam's direction, the local ionosphere's density, and the orbiter's electrical potential compared with that of the ionosphere.

The RETE experiment, led by Dr. Marino Dobrowolny of the Italian Space Agency, will provide information about the electrical potential of the ionized gas or "plasma," sheath that will surround the tethered satellite during its deployed operations.

First, it should be noted that all of this data comes on Sunday, February 25, between 6:00 a.m. and 8:00 a.m. long before the "tether incident." I call NASA's fancy physics here the "black hole" because it will do the same thing to most people's minds that black holes do to light: absorb them all into their false presentation.

The first observation is that, " This gave scientists and crew members an idea of how the Shuttle's environment might react to water dumps released while the tethered satellite is deployed." This is to suggest that the shuttle will release water dumps while the satellite is deployed. The report then suggests, "The water molecules in this cloud exchanged electrical charges with the surrounding ionized oxygen and formed a ring shape which could be easily distinguished from the ionized gas background around Columbia." At first glance, this sounds like a plausible explanation by NASA for the "ring shapes" we witnessed during the "tether incident," but it is illogical.

When the "tether incident" happened, the shuttle Columbia was 77 and drifting to 100 nautical miles away. How did a "water dump" ionize to form a "ring shape," travel 100 miles away in seconds (an impossible speed for water) and then pass "behind" the tethered satellite revealing itself to be 2-3 miles in diameter. The amount of water needed to form a ring 2 miles in diameter, let alone fifty of them, would overburden the shuttle with so much water weight, it would have never been able to launch and carry such an astounding amount of water, let alone the crew, into space to conduct the experiment. But that is not all that is terribly wrong with NASA's new reasoning.

NASA also suggests in this report that, "Previous measurements indicated that a thin electron beam emitted from the orbiter quickly expands in width to form a cylinder." Since there were no cylinder's (only circles) in the "tether incident," one can safely assume that the cylinder shape must have something to do with the ionized gas around the tether cable itself, giving off a glow (making the tether more visible).

If NASA was suggesting that the alleged UFOs in the "tether incident" were ionized gas balls, "surrounding ionized oxygen and formed a ring shape," such as a plasma, the largest "black hole" in their reasoning would emerge. Ionized gases are like the neon gas in neon light tubes or florescent light tubes which become luminous when electrically charged particles activate the gas. For a gas to become ionized and illuminate, energy and gas would be needed.

First, the gas in the satellite was nitrogen. We do know from the article in the United Press International, the gas that leaked from the satellite was nitrogen. It was a small satellite so the amount of nitrogen it had on board couldn't have been enough to form a single, 2-3 mile wide circle, let alone fifty of them, as witnessed in the video of the incident. The balls of light with clear architecture (portals) did not suddenly form as the alleged gas leaked from the satellite and then fly away, rather they cam from afar and then gathered around the satellite (suggesting their origin was not relative to the satellite), as the report states that, "a thin electron beam emitted from the orbiter quickly expands in width to form a cylinder."

If NASA is suggesting in this report that the balls of light witnessed during the "tether incident" were merely "ionized plasma," (gas) and we let NASA try and tell us they had enough gas to fill 50, 2-3 mile wide balls of light with gas (impossible), we are still left with the real "black hole." That is, plasma cannot form a perfect, angular architecture, cannot bend in sharp distinct angles (the square portals), and cannot hold any real shape (even a perfect circle) when it is not confined in a containment system.

The round, enormous sized discs witnessed during the "tether incident" had obvious square portals revealing structure. The square or triangular angles in the portals reveal structure that a plasma could not form unless the plasma were confined into a structure of that shape. For example, a neon gas can take the shape of a neon light tube. The tube is the container. If the gas was free in space, it would probably resemble a cloud and dissipate under the influence of intense solar radiation. Therefore, a container with the same shape as the circular objects, with their square portals would have to be the next reasonable assumption to explain this. Such a container of 2-3 miles in diameter would have to be some kind of spacecraft or living entity's (living plasma) phenomenal membrane.

I asked Dr. Bogdan Castle Maglich, the M.I.T. PhD nuclear fusion physicist, about the tape. I asked him, "Can a plasma form a perfect circle?" He answered, "Only if it was a low energy plasma. Yes it could." Judging the speed of some of these objects (against 12 miles of tether per second of distance) to be travelling up to 35,000 mph, I could not deduce that they were low energy plasma. When I mentioned the clear angular portals in the circles, and asked him if a plasma could make such formations, he thought it was impossible and alarming.

The Tokomak fusion reactor at Princeton Plasma Physics Lab was another good example. The multi-billion dollar fusion machine was essentially a confinement device (container) for a high-energy plasma (gas). Temperatures in the plasma of 100 million degrees Centigrade would be reached. If the gas was free of the containment system, it wouldn't ignite nor would it be possible to confine it in such an architecture. It would form an amorphous cloud. So how could NASA say it was able to create a multi-billion dollar confined, 2-3 miles-wide plasma that had clear shape, control and architecture in space, let alone fifty of them? If they could, how did they ship the 2-3 mile-wide containers into space and then fill them with gas (plasma) and then ionize them?

As the investigation reveals, it was all impossible what NASA was saying. The very fact that NASA pretended to know so much about what they were doing with the STS-75 tether experiment "after the fact" contradicts how little the Columbia crew knew about the amazing alleged UFOs when NASA, Huntsville operator asked them, "We see a long light and a lot of objects swimming in the foreground. Can you describe what we are seeing?" The response was, "stray light getting washed out." They didn't say, "Yes, this is the Tether Optical Phenomenon caused by ionized gas and water dumps" did they? That's because NASA made up all that fancy, inaccurate physics "after the fact" to have an answer for the public.

As we will next examine, because the experiment went awry when the tether broke, one can't assume that NASA was able to conduct their experiments with "electron guns" between the shuttle and the satellite along the tether (formerly linking the two craft) because the tether was broken. Electrons wouldn't flow through the tether and into the shuttle for data collection because the cable wasn't connected to the shuttle any more. Because the connection was broken, all of their fancy experiments couldn't theoretically work. So what caused the sudden appearance of over 50, fast and slow moving mysterious objects? The STS-75 Day 4 report continues with Sunday, February 25, 1996, 6:00 p.m. STS-75 Payload Status Report # 06:

Today marked a major milestone as the STS-75 crew aboard the Space Shuttle Columbia began deploying the joint NASA/Italian Space Agency Tethered Satellite System (TSS) on schedule at 2:45 p.m. CST. The world watched as the satellite smoothly and gently lifted from its cradle atop the latticework boom that previously had been extended some 40 feet (11.3 meters) out of Columbia's cargo bay. The crew continues carefully unreeling the satellite on its slender tether. Mission Specialist Jeffry Hoffman reported that "the satellite is rock solid," an observation confirmed by downlinked telemetry being viewed by the TSS ground crew.

On Sunday, February 25, 1996, 9:30 p.m. STS-75 MCC Status Report # 08 reports:

The tether on the Italian Tethered satellite broke about 7:30 p.m. CST Sunday as the satellite was nearing the full extent of its deployment from the shuttle. The satellite, which was nearing the end of its planned 12.8 mile distance, immediately began accelerating away from Columbia at a rapid rate as a result of normal orbital forces. TSS is separating from Columbia at a rate of 420 miles each 90 minute orbit.

The tether apparently snapped near the top of the 39-foot TSS boom in Columbia's cargo bay. Neither the astronauts nor the Space Shuttle were ever in any danger.

Following the break, Mission Control asked the astronauts to record television of the boom and broken tether for post flight analysis.

That was the end of the report. There is no mention in this report of the amazing phenomenon that occurred after the break when the tethered satellite drifted 77 nautical miles away. We just know, from the report, that all of this was being filmed "for post flight analysis." The reports that required access codes were obviously "classified." Those reports, and only the highest level security clearance could access the ultimate report, had to reveal the incident. I searched NASA's website for more. What I found was three still photographs of the tether at 100 nautical miles with the alleged UFOs around it: a black and white photo-frame right out of the video. While it was proof enough for me, the dots just looked like big, round stars. Only the video could prove that they were moving. The still-photo also didn't show the alleged UFOs in a zoomed "close-up."

When we applied the "Alternative Space Program" theory to the size, energy and magnitude of the UFOs witnessed in the "tether incident," it clearly appeared that NASA was encountering a genuine extraterrestrial contact phenomenon. These craft or living entities were too enormous, interdimensional and beyond current physics to be manmade. If the "Alternative Space Program" did exist, we deducted that it could only be drawing on the technology of such advanced civilizations.

From all the incidents I had seen on the Martyn Stubbs NASA video, our research group always found NASA's obvious lies to cover up what was really happening. Because they lied so often, their credibility was waning. Martyn still had not shown me his most advanced footage. The tether was still just the beginning of the best footage.

IV - STAR SEQUENCE

For example of another one of NASA's blatant lies, there is another sequence on the Martyn Stubbs, NASA video where the space shuttle has its cameras pointed straight down at the Earth. It appears to be looking at a large city. The camera is obviously hand-held because it is a little shaky. Suddenly a bright light goes by between the shuttle and the city far below. It is important to note the shuttle's altitude is usually at ~300 miles above the earth according to Dr. Nuth. If an airline passenger 747 was flying over a city at 35,000 feet, you would not see the 747 at all. It is too far away.

The light passes by and the NASA shuttle crew member responds by saying, "There's a light going by on the ground there." He then covers his track by saying, "It could have been a Star Bill" before he gets an answer. Then another light goes by. There is no answer.

Everyone knows that the sun is the only star in the solar system. If the cameras are pointed down at the earth from ~300 miles above it, there can't be a star between the shuttle and the earth because the nearest star (the sun) is 93 million miles away. The only alternative explanation would have to be that the word "star" is code for UFO or something else. How can the public have any trust in an agency that lies constantly when it encounters unknown phenomena? One has to assume that if Martyn Stubbs recorded this kind of revolutionary NASA UFO footage, then NASA must have even better video footage and perhaps film footage of these events. As Dr. Nuth pointed out in his last letter to me, "There are at least four cameras mounted in the shuttle bay."

V - ICE CRYSTAL SEQUENCE

This is a relatively simple part of the video to observe. It is too simple and that is what is peculiar about it. We are told by NASA control in Huntsville, Alabama that, "There seems to be a lot of moonlight reflecting off the water. Is that a real picture, or are we just getting some video fuzz?" The objects referred to as "moonlight reflecting off the water" are clearly objects that are between the shuttle and the Earth down below. There are a large number of these amorphously shaped objects and they shimmer and pulse like diamonds.

There is a long pause before anyone of the crew members answer NASA control which is very suspicious.

The answer finally comes, "Those are the ice particles we were dumping out earlier." NASA control answers, "That's a nice combination of the moonlight reflecting off of the water (oceans) and the ice crystals."

NASA had lied too many times in the past and I wasn't going to give them an inch in this investigation when it came to lies. Judging by the enormity of ice that NASA allegedly says was "dumped out earlier," one would have to question where the shuttle produces so much ice. Is it a giant snow cone machine in space that dumps huge ice crystals several times each day? You need water to make ice. Where did the shuttle carry so much water (weight) and why does it make ice out of its water supply (presumably for drinking, bathing and experiments) and dump it all out? There were so many large alleged ice crystals in this sequence, I couldn't help but poke fun at NASA once again.

I decided to investigate the entire model of the space shuttle and see if I could find where on the shuttle this enormity of ice was being made and why the astronauts would dump out so much ice. It seemed like an awful waste of water considering how much energy it takes for the space shuttle to carry all this water out into space just so that the astronauts can make snow cones and throw them out the window.

I found a space shuttle manual on NASA's website on the internet. This was easy. Everything on the space shuttle was listed here for anyone's perusal. I studied the section on "Supply and Waste Water." What I found was very peculiar.

First of all there are four supply water tanks on the shuttle and one waste water tank, each of which have a capacity of 160 pounds of water. Each tank is 35.5 inches in length and 15.5 inches in diameter. The small sizes of these four tanks show us how heavy water is equal to its mass storage space. If all four of the supply water tanks were dumped overboard, we would expect to see four water balls 35.5 by 15.5 inches in size each. This is the first set of facts.

How does the shuttle carry its water? There are three fuel cell power plants that generate a maximum of 25 pounds of potable water per hour. The product water from all three fuel cell power plants flows to a single water relief control panel. The water can then be directed to the water storage tanks.

When the water made in the fuel cell power plants is too hydrogen rich (H20), the excess hydrogen is separated from the water by two hydrogen separators. The hydrogen separators consist of a matrix of silver palladium tubes, which have an affinity for hydrogen. The hydrogen is dumped overboard through a vacuum vent. So we know that hydrogen gas can get dumped overboard. Hydrogen gas is very volatile and must dissolve or burn up very quickly under the influence of intense radiation from the sun.

The next thing I learned about water on the space shuttle is that it can be dumped overboard also. But there is a surprise. The manual clearly stated that potable water from tank A or B can be dumped overboard, if necessary, through a dump isolation valve and dump valve. Potable water from tank C or D can also be dumped overboard, if necessary, through the crossover valve and through the sump isolation valve.

A contingency crosstie valve, in the supply water overboard dump line between the dump isolation valve and dump valve, permits the joining of the waste water system through a flexible hose to supply water system "for emergency dumping of waste water" through the supply water dump or use of waste water for the flash evaporators.

This reveals that water is only dumped in case of an emergency as the manual further states, "The EMU dump will be used only if an EVA is required."

Of course the astronauts on the shuttle don't make a habit of dumping out water just for fun. If they did, they would be out of their own water supply very quickly.

As to where the shuttle produces "ice crystals" that we were told by the astronauts on these missions, "were being dumped out" of the shuttle, where are they manufactured? Nowhere on the shuttle manual could I find a freezer unit or a facility for making ice. In fact, it is so cold up there in space (-273 degrees C), who needs and ice machine. I even found that water is heated on the shuttle to prevent lines from freezing.

As I presented earlier and confirmed with Dr. Nuth at NASA, space is a dichotomy with regards to its temperature. Space is cold but as soon as any gas, liquid or solid object is exposed to bare space, the intense radiation from the sun quickly causes heat to be formed and very fast nuclear and chemical reactions take place.

The question about the alleged "ice crystals" is that we know that small pieces of ice (even a few meters in diameter) could not survive the intense radiation from the sun and stars in space for very long. In fact, what we were told by the astronauts on these missions was that the alleged ice crystals we were seeing were being dumped out of the shuttle when in truth, they rarely dump out water. Water is not ice. If the ice or water were dumped from the shuttle in an emergency water release situation, it should dissolve very quickly, yet these alleged ice crystals do not.

There are several segments on the NASA video where we can see enormous bodies of ice floating by, many of which appear to be larger than the four 35.5 by 15.5 inch water tanks on the shuttle. And there are a lot more than four of these enormous ice crystals on space shuttle missions on the video. In once scene, there are over 100 of these large objects. Some of them seem to be enormous chunks of ice, perhaps, judging by 20 years of experience looking through camera lenses, these may be five to ten feet in diameter or even much greater (depending on distance from the camera).

It would be cause for alarm to suggest that these are possible "small comets" because of what devastation they would cause upon inevitable impact with the Earth. There is no greater mystery to me as to what these objects may be. Because the cameras do not zoom in on these objects, we cannot be certain if they are the same kind of UFOs that we witnessed on the other footage.

VI - STS-80 FORMATION OVER AFRICA

This next sequence will provide the investigation with a piece of evidence equal to the "tether incident" in paramount significance. It will reveal intelligence, architecture, design, timing and precision of communication.

Watching the video, we could see a number of glowing objects in the distance. One of the objects (right side of screen) was pulsating very rapidly as it flies above the Earth horizon at the space shuttle's altitude. This sequence is very important because it provides the viewer with clear distinctions between Dr. Joseph Nuth, III's "dust bunnies" in the near-field focus of the camera or shuttle window and real objects outside and in the far distance from the shuttle. There are a few spots, which appear to be on the shuttle window. The camera is being hand-held and moves from time to time. The spots on the window move exactly in time with the camera pans. This shows Dr. Nuth as being correct with regards to some real "dust bunnies."

The glowing objects in the background in space move very differently and are free of the movements of the camera. The balls of light gather in a circle in the far distance. The circle is slowly becoming completed. It is not a perfect circle, but it is close. With great timing and precision, when one of the balls of light reaches its position in the circle, it lights up extra bright exactly as it finds its final and fixed position. Now, we see a ghost-like circular object traverse from the above-foreground position to the far distance. When this object reaches the very center of the circle, it lights up with an extra luminosity signifying that it has reached its destination: the center of the circle.

The very fact that these objects gather in a circle is incredible if one considers the unlikely premise that Dr. Nuth's alleged "floating debris" in space could do the same thing. But even more unlikely for "floating debris" is the possibility that these objects could flash with an extra intensity of light once they reached their resting and fixed positions. At least three of them do this. Finally, the object that flies into the center of the circle flashes with extra-intense light to announce its arrival to the center of the circle. This reveals a plan to form a circle, timing to announce positions being completed and the final position is reached as the center of the circle.

While the chances of natural "floating debris" accomplishing this remarkable formation, and then holding the positions without continuing in a drift was sufficient in proving to our research group that this was a planned event. But who planned it? NASA didn't say anything about it in the live commentary that they were planning an alignment of particles. They did, however, film the entire event and broadcast it live to the world.

Just following the event, camera's are switched to what appear to be the payload bay cameras. We hear a woman say, "Go for Wake Shield." We then see two round balls of light with dots in the center of them arrive from different directions. They burst out into space away from the Earth at an accelerated speed. Was this "Wake Shield?"

I researched the word "Wake Shield" on NASA's website. I found out that this was the name of a satellite that was being launched on this STS-80 mission. What we had just witnessed had nothing to do with the satellite Wake Shield. Here is what NASA described about two satellites being launched on this STS-80, Columbia, ORFEUS-SPAS-2/WAKE SHIELD Facility-3, KSC Release No. 124-96, October, 1996 Report:

While ORFEUS-SPAS orbits the Earth, the crew on flight day 4 will use the orbiter's robot arm to deploy the second major payload, Wake Shield Facility-3, a 12-foot-diameter (3.6-meter) stainless steel disc, which has flown twice before.

While low Earth orbital space is considered a moderate vacuum, it still has atmospheric traces that could contaminate crystal growth. While sweeping through space at an orbital speed of approximately 18,000 miles per hour (28,962 kilometers per hour), WSF brushes aside these trace particles and forms a wake, much like the wake of a boat in the water. This creates an ultra-vacuum – far superior to vacuums created in Laboratories on earth – where near perfect crystals of semiconductor compounds such as gallium arsenide can be grown.
During its three days of operations, up to seven thin films are scheduled to be grown on the wake side of the approximately 4,600-pound (2,086-kilogram) platform. This method of growing crystals in an atom-by-

atom, layer-by-layer manner in a vacuum environment is called molecular beam epitaxy.

While most electronic components used today are made of the semiconductor silicon, other types of semiconductor materials – particularly compound semiconductors – have the potential of producing higher-performance electronic and opto-electronic devices. Epitaxial thin film materials grow on WSF could result in higher-efficiency infrared lasers, higher frequency transistors for personal communications systems, higher-efficiency energy converters for hybrid electric vehicles and remote electric power systems, and low-noise transistors for wireless communications.

WSF will fly at a distance of about 20-25 nautical miles (37-46 kilometers) behind Columbia and no less than 25 nautical miles (46 kilometers) from ORFEUS-SPAS before its retrieval by Columbia on flight day 7.

The Wake Shield facility was designed, built and is operated by a NASA Commercial Space Center, the Space Vacuum Epitaxy Center at the University of Houston, in conjunction with its industrial partner, Space Industries Inc. of Houston. It previously flew on STS-60 in 1994 and STS-69 in 1995.

The Martyn Stubbs, NASA video then showed video footage of the two satellites Wake Shield and ORFEUS SPAS as they trailed behind the space shuttle Columbia. They appear as very large objects, which follow each other at a perfect and constant rate of drift-speed. Neither of the two objects drift apart, and follow Galileo and Newtonian Laws of Gravity perfectly. This was a good piece of video to study what a satellite looks like and how they behave so perfectly in space. None of the other incidents viewed so far look anything like satellites.

The other satellite being launched was very interesting for our investigation to study. It is called ORFEUS SPAS-2. Here is what was written by NASA about this satellite on their publicly posted report:

The primary objectives of the 80th Space Shuttle mission are the deployment, operation and retrieval of two scientific satellites which have flown before.

110

The Orbiting Retrievable Far and Extreme Ultraviolet Sectrometer-Shuttle Pallet Satellite-2 (ORFEUS-SPAS-2) will be deployed first to make observations and take measurements of celestial objects that emit most of their light or radiation in the invisible, ultraviolet band of the electromagnetic spectrum. STS-80 will be the second flight of ORFEUS-SPAS, which is a cooperative project of NASA and the German Space Agency (DARA). ORFEUS-SPAS will fly free of the shuttle for slightly more than 13 days before it is retrieved for the return to Earth.

About seven hours after launch, ORFEUS-SPAS-2 will be deployed to study life cycle of stars and the nature of the interstellar medium. Many of the celestial objects it will look at have never or rarely been observed in the far and extreme ultraviolet range. This part of the electromagnetic spectrum is obscured from ground-based observations by Earth's atmosphere.

The free-flying SPAS platform, which is abut the size of the flatbed of a large pickup truck, will operate some 40 miles (64 kilometers) behind the Shuttle before its retrieval and rebirthing in the payload bay on flight day 14.

Two spectrographs, the German-built far Ultraviolet Spectrograph (FUV) and the American-designed Extreme Ultraviolet Spectrograph (EUV), will share the single main German-built ORFEUS telescope. Its 39-inch-diameter (1-meter) mirror is coated with iridium to improve its light-gathering power in the ultraviolet. A third spectrograph, the American-built Interstellar Medium Absorption Profile Spectrograph (IMAPS), is attached to the German ASTRO-SPAS platform. All of the instruments flew on the first ORFEUS-SPAS mission, STS-51 in 1993.

The third letter written to me from Dr. Joseph Nuth, III, NASA Head of Astrochemistry had given the investigation a clue as to where NASA and the Department of Defense was looking for the mysterious, unidentified flying objects, "and his previous (~1985) observations using the DE spacecraft's UV camera, few other people agree with him."

This showed that Dr. Louis A. Frank's mysterious objects were only visible in the Ultraviolet range of light, exactly where ORFEUS-SPAS-2 was looking. Was it a coincidence?

Coincidence wasn't likely since there were too many other areas of the radiating energy spectrum to observe. NASA knew they couldn't find the unidentified objects in the infrared radiation spectrum when Dr. Nuth wrote, "The reasons are many, but the best center on the fact that these objects should have been detected on several other satellites such as COBE, IRAS and ISO. These satellites have instruments that are very sensitive to radiation in the infrared region. These fluffy, house-sized objects should bee at a temperature near 300K or even higher as they near the earth since very fluffy objects are much better absorbers in the visible than the are emitters in the infrared. They should therefore be infrared beacons because they are so very close. Yet no other satellite has ever seen evidence for these objects. This includes a vast array of DoD satellites as far as I can learn."

Now that NASA had eliminated the other spectrums of radio and infrared, and this investigation clearly demonstrated that the UV range is the more energetic of the measurable light spectrum (x-rays and gamma rays above it), was it the next obvious place to be looking for intelligent, extraterrestrial life or spacecraft? Was ORFEUS-SPAS-2 looking in the far and extreme UV range just to study stars like the report read?

If the Department of Defense was looking for Dr. Louis A. Frank's alleged "small comets" on infrared satellite cameras and couldn't find them, and they knew that Dr. Frank had seen them in the UV range, wouldn't more precise UV range cameras on satellites be the next logical position to investigate the mysterious phenomenon? As we had earlier demonstrated, visible and UV light energy would most likely be radiating from a craft or life form capable of near-light or beyond-light speeds. This is because UV and visible light are more energetic than infrared and radio waves. It takes greater energy (as in the energy source of a spacecraft) to travel at or above light speeds. If a UFO were to travel from the nearest stars to our solar system, they would have to be capable of such speeds. This was the right place for NASA to be looking and they knew it. ORFEUS-SPAS-2 was possibly looking at stars and unidentified object phenomena at the same time.

The STS-80 report revealed that, "The ORFEUS telescope, with its 39-inch-diameter (1-meter) mirror is coated with iridium to improve its light-gathering power in the ultraviolet." This may also have been applied to the "special filters" on the video camera and possible "special sensitive films" used to see objects, possibly the UFOs seen on the NASA video, that are invisible to the human eye. The invisible range of light to the human eye is proposed to exist, yet exist in another dimension. The UV range would be a higher, or more energetic dimension than light which is visible to most humans, and infrared light (invisible to humans) that is visible to reptiles.

Chapter Five
The NASA Investigation Intensifies

"Many people would sooner die than think; In fact, they do so" –
Bertrand Russell

I – Contacting NASA Astronaut Edgar Mitchell

Edgar Mitchell is a former astronaut who walked on the moon in 1971. He has since become a public advocate in the growing worldwide UFO movement. He speaks at UFO conventions all around the world. In a 1998 London Times news article, Mitchell is described as believing that "Aliens have landed on Earth" and he has "Intensified his campaign to persuade Washington to acknowledge life beyond our skies."

Mitchell argues that life is almost certain to exist on any other planet with a supportive environment. Some physicists, he points out, now believe it is possible to travel faster than light, even if humble Earthlings have yet to achieve it.

He is 90% certain that many of the thousands of UFOs recorded since the 1940s belonged to visitors from another planet. Although some have been delusions and others natural phenomena, too many remain unexplained, he said. "This suggests there are humanoids manning craft which have characteristics not in the arsenal of any nation on Earth that we know of. That is very alarming," he said.

Edgar Mitchell holds a Ph.D. from M.I.T., and stands to be a perfect candidate for this particular NASA UFO investigation. He is also a consultant to the X-Files, the cult television series from Hollywood. Mitchell says his research – including conversations with people who have worked in intelligence agencies and military groups – has convinced him that the American government has covered up the truth about UFOs for 50 years. He is trying to persuade Congress to grant his sources immunity to tell the real story of events such as the alleged Roswell incident – the crash of a flying saucer in New Mexico in 1947.

I wrote Dr. Mitchell in October, 1999 and told him about the footage. I was sure he would be interested to see it. He wrote me back by e-mail the following letter on October 17, 1999:

David Sereda, I will look at the letters you mention. But I do not know Dr. Nuth. Regarding videotapes, in this day of digital processes of images, demonstrating provenance for video is vital, but it is almost impossible to do. So I will listen but be hard to convince about your video.

He then gave me his address and I sent him the video. I was anxiously awaiting to get a response from him that would be positive and in favor of the UFO theory. I told Mike Boyle and Martyn Stubbs that I had made actual contact with Edgar Mitchell and that he would be looking at the video. Martyn was as excited as any space enthusiast 1960s child would be who witnessed the launch of Mitchell's Apollo mission to the moon in 1971. Martyn and I shared a profound moment, we thought, that had been both of our dreams since we were children. We thought that Edgar Mitchell would be so impressed with what he saw, that he would want to come and meet both of us to discuss the release of the material to the world. We both awaited his answer.

On November 24, 1999 Edgar Mitchell wrote me the following letter:

David Sereda, Yes, I have received your film and reviewed it and the info package you provided. I see utterly nothing about the tether incident that is particularly interesting. If there is more revealing footage then I will look at it. However, I have looked at many feet of space film, and have yet to see only one that has anything worth looking into regarding UFO appearances. Edgar Mitchell.

I could not accept that such a great proponent of UFOs was so adamantly against the suggestion that these giant circles passing behind the tethered satellite were UFOs. He was shrugging off the most astounding piece of video ever witnessed of UFOs in the history of the space program. I couldn't believe it. It was outraged. When I shared the news with my partners, they thought, and I shared the thought, that Edgar Mitchell might be an insider to the UFO movement sent by NASA to protect them from any possible implications of real UFOs. This theory would make Edgar Mitchell as a pretender to be in support of UFO research while he and NASA both knew why he was really inside the UFO movement: search and destroy all real evidence and also always inform NASA what they may be up against and give them time to prepare.

I decided to try and argue the points with Mitchell more precisely. He wrote me back almost right away:

David, At first glance they are just particles...perhaps outgassed, I do not know. But I certainly would look for a more prosaic explanation than UFOs. If you have a better film, I will look, but I am not very optimistic they are anything exotic. EDM.

I wrote Edgar Mitchell right away the following letter:

Dear Edgar Mitchell, First I thank you for taking a look at this footage. Did you see the whole tether? At first glance they do look like "just particles" yes. But when the camera zooms in on them, they clearly are not just particles. There are over 50 of them in once scene. Because of the 12-mile length of the tether, and the fact that they pass behind it, we can measure enormous sizes to these objects: the largest 2-3 miles in diameter. These could not be particles near the camera on the shuttle because they are over 70 miles away. Did you see this part of the tape? This makes outgassing impossible and ionized gases impossible, as the physics for ionized gasses would not allow them to make such precise form and architecture (I checked this fact with a M.I.T. nuclear physicist). I do, however, have other footage that is equally important. I will send you a much better tape with the tether and other instances. Again, after viewing all the footage I send you, I would still be interested in your opinions. Thank you very much for your time.

Dr. Mitchell's response to this letter arrived on December 1, 1999:

David, Okay, I will look at the tape, but be hard to convince that anything of significance is occurring. I am not impressed by physicists from M.I.T. or anywhere else in this arena. Blobs of light routinely appear on film if being reflected from some small object in space. Look up in the sky in the early morning and see the reflections from a satellite as the sun comes up...the reflection is many times larger in apparent size than the actual object. Star light is the same. Distant stars would not be visible at all except for the spreading and diffusion of the light, which makes them visible. EDM

Well, that was the end of Edgar Mitchell in my investigation, I thought. If his arguments were at least interesting, I would have continued. To insult M.I. T. physicists was almost suggesting anger on his part of the investigation, but angry about what? Was he trying his best to divert me away from believing that these were really UFOs? I had to persist with him for another letter. I told him that these objects could not be space debris or particles because they were too large and their minimum sizes could be calculated as the UFOs passed behind the tether. He wrote me back the following letter on December 3, 1999:

David Sereda, I remain open minded, but I saw nothing on the tape you sent that had sharply defined edges in the vicinity of or passing behind the tether. The only NASA footage that had anything of real interest to me has already been shown on TV——I don't remember which program, or now which STS flight it was. Also, in the footage of the tether, the commentator on the spacecraft is making a running commentary. Were really anything of significance in space around the tether at that time, don't you think they would have been saying something about it? If they were as big as you say, they would have been visible to the naked eye and surely reported——not ignored as seems to be the case. You comment about no infrared image. Of course not. If nothing is there, how could there be an infrared image? Edgar M.

The first point here shows obvious denial of obvious facts: that Edgar Mitchell cannot see that the alleged UFOs are clearly passing "behind" the tether which is 77-100 nautical miles away from the shuttle.

I feel that after seeing this tape over 100 times, and having used cameras for over 20 years, that I have never seen a phenomenon that can cause an object in the foreground (the tether) to reverse positions with an object in the background (the UFOs). The light reflecting off of the tether or radiating from the alleged ionized gas sheath around it is obscuring the light coming from the alleged disc-shaped UFOs. That clearly makes the UFOs background objects to the tether (as the foreground object). There is no good argument against these simple physics. It is clear, yet Edgar Mitchell is denying these obvious facts. This is grounds to suggest that he is deliberately trying to avoid the truth for reasons that can only be hypothesized: Does Edgar Mitchell still work for NASA? Is he trying to protect the Agency's position on this while he merely pretends to be a UFO advocate? He was starting to look very suspicious to our research group.

About his comments that the astronauts should be actually talking about these objects, as if they would talk about them as UFOs while being broadcast live to the world? It would only make sense that to protect national security interests that NASA would communicate on their DoD alternate channels to speak about secure information. Of course they would use such channels to speak about an event like this. There is mostly silence on the part of the astronauts during these missions. Are the astronauts really that quiet or are they talking on secure DoD channels?

Edgar Mitchell's comments about there being no infrared image meaning that this means "If nothing is there, how could there be an infrared image" I would have to say that he does not understand light theory very well. Or, he may not have had access to objects that are observed in the UV range only. Perhaps these new observations can only be described by quantum physics, an area of physics that is making a revival today but may not be well accepted by Edgar Mitchell.

I decided to challenge Dr. Edgar Mitchell on another obvious fact about the STS-75 tether incident: that the alleged UFOs were all travelling at different rates of speed. Gallileo's (Newton) law of gravity says that all objects, regardless of their weight or mass, fall through gravity at the same rate of speed. Gravity is also a pull in a constant direction with regards to the Earth's gravity so all objects falling into gravity should be falling at the same speed and in the same constant direction spiraling down towards the Earth. In the tether incident, Gallielo's law of gravity and motion is broken: the alleged UFOs are all moving at different speeds and in different directions. This implies that they have internal energy, since the only way for an object to accomplish the goals of breaking Gallileo's law of gravity and motion is to have internal energy and propulsion. I wrote this letter to Dr. Mitchell and he refused to answer it. That to me was enough to prove that Edgar Mitchell was not really interested in helping to expose the fact that these objects were behaving like spacecraft rather than particles. NASA was trying their best to cover this all up and he was in on it.

When I shared this information with my partners, Mike Boyle and Martyn Stubbs, they began to detect danger. What if NASA and the National Security Agency (NSA) would be onto us? What if they felt this information was so sensitive, they would poison us, threaten us or even take our lives. Was it curious enough that Martyn Stubbs developed a brain tumor while he was working on this project. Mike Boyle complained of being approached by some people in a vehicle one night who then reached out of the car and sprayed some chemical on him and drove away. Since that day, Mike Boyle wasn't feeling very well at all.

I, on the other hand, didn't care if I lived or died. I was willing to die to find the truth. Perhaps that is what it takes to know the truth. Besides, I always wanted to see if the "men in black" were real. I would get on the phone with NASA and talk to persons there about their own footage, write them letters with my actual return address being completely open with them. So far, no one has shown up in a black sedan to take me away. Perhaps the space agency really isn't hiding anything. Perhaps those who know the truth inside NASA don't even share it with other employees, including with the heads of certain scientific departments.

If there was a conspiracy at the agency to stop the proliferation of this material to the American public, they would go all the way to the media and ask them to prevent its release also. In the summer of 1999, my friend Amber had got me a meeting at Davis Entertainment, an affiliate of 20th Century Fox with Vice President of Series Television Paul Spadone. Paul had two assistants present, Jessica Stamer and

John Weber, a consultant to Davis Entertainment on real life x-files. I brought with me my friend Amber and another partner and documentary film producer named Brenda.

After presenting the NASA video footage in the meeting, the project was a 90% go-ahead. Paul and Jessica loved the project. We were all so excited. Jessica thought that they would ask the X-Files character Dana Scully (Jillian Anderson) to host the show as a scrutinizing "devil's advocate" and get famed real life x-files radio talk show host Art Bell to play the protagonist who would present the new amazing NASA video footage to the world. In the end, the public could decide for themselves if it was all real. At the end of the meeting, it looked like they wanted to go with the project. John Webber, Paul's real life x-files advisor, said that he had some reservations about the footage.

Within three days, Davis Entertainment decided against doing the show. It was cancelled by the superiors in the company without those superiors ever actually seeing the footage for themselves. What happened? Was there a directive at Fox to prevent the public from seeing this new and amazing video footage of alleged NASA UFOs? Or, was it purely a marketing decision? We could not know for sure that there was a conspiracy, only that their interest went from 90% all the way down to zero in 48 hours.

I then had a new meeting at a new broadcast network that I will keep the name of confidential for their own fears of having seen this tape. I went into this meeting in Santa Monica, California in the summer of 1999. I showed the video to a group of over 15 persons associated with this new broadcast network.

After seeing the footage, I was asked to replay and replay the many incidents on the tape. People were astounded. 90 percent of all persons present wanted to broadcast the tape through their network. One lone man, who was a long time UFO enthusiast, convinced the network executives that the NSA would close down their station for broadcasting this NASA UFO material. It would destroy the network. After a long discussion with the CEO of the company and this one man, they decided against it. Could this have been the same reason that 20th Century Fox also said "no?"

If all of these persons were afraid of the NSA, why hadn't the NSA come to stop me from exposing this secret videotape to the world? Or had they done that by controlling people's minds already with the almighty fear of death?

In 1999, in Vancouver, British Columbia, the Hollywood North producers were busy filming a new film directed by Brian DePalma called "Mission To Mars." The director's brother, Bruce DePalma was an M.I.T. Ph.D. electrical engineer and physicist. He was working on perpetual motion generators and involved in conspiracy theories. In particular, he was involved in the mystery of STS-75. Apparently, Bruce DePalma was speaking on the world famous Art Bell radio show after the STS-75 incident and experiment had gone awry. He knew something about that mission and discussed it on Art Bell's show. He died not long after he did that show. Was NASA and the NSA threatened by anyone who might have compelling evidence about STS-75 and the tether incident?

I could only assume that by Edgar Mitchell's anger and repressive ideas and stories like Bruce DePalma's that our whole research group might be in grave danger. Still, I was not afraid of death. I wanted to know the truth and get it out to the people of this world.

II - Contacting NASA press correspondent James Oberg

Martyn Stubbs' number one protagonist for the media for NASA on the subject of these UFOs was James Oberg. James Oberg is NASA's acclaimed critic that convinced the news media's world that when astronaut John Glenn saw glowing balls of light outside of his Gemini lunar module that he wasn't seeing a new form of life in space rather his own urine that was dumped out of the capsule. As if John Glenn would admire his own urine floating in space and mistake it for some kind of phenomenon. What the public did not know was that back then, there was no room for astronauts to flush their waste in a deep space toilet in such a small spacecraft. In fact, because the missions were so short, there was no need to have such facilities. While the public remained ignorant of the mechanical facts of the Gemini spacecraft, most of them bought James Oberg's stories.

James Oberg was also the one to convince the world that Jack Kasher's STS-45 NASA alleged UFOs were just pieces of space debris that got caught in the line of the shuttle altitude thruster engines and went flying off when the engines were fired. But James Oberg doesn't make these stories up himself. It was NASA who was telling him what to say to the American People. The following is a news article about previous NASA footage of alleged UFOs by James Oberg at ABC news:

STS-48 - Science Battles
Wishful Thinking
By Jim Oberg

Special to ABCNEWS.com

2-20-99

As humans explore space, it's reasonable to imagine that other beings in the universe are doing the same. Encountering explorers from other planets have been a staple of science fiction for decades. Videotapes from space shuttle missions have persuaded some folks that NASA astronauts have already encountered alien visitors. On the space shuttle mission STS-48 in September 1991, a TV onboard Discovery spotted moving white dots suddenly changing direction when a flash of light appeared. Although nearby debris frequently appears on shuttle videos, the combination of flares, streaks and changing directions grabbed imaginations. Answering a congressional query the following month on behalf of a curious constituent, NASA had four Houston experts - including one astronaut, astronomer Karl Henize - examine the videos. "The objects seen are [Discovery]-generated debris, illuminated by the sun," they reported. "The flicker of light is the result of firing of the attitude thrusters on [Discovery], and the abrupt motions of the particles result from the impact of gas from the thrusters." That didn't wash for some viewers, who believed they were seeing alien visitors or Star Wars-like battles. [*Nearby drifting debris has been hit by jet pulses on other shuttle flights. Here's an example from STS-63 in February 1995. Popular Interpretation Enthusiasm for the UFO interpretation of space pictures isn't restricted to a narrow band of crackpots, as any Web search demonstrates. Mainstream writers and major TV networks also promulgate these misinterpretations. Aside from enhancing the public's paranoia about government cover-ups, it can have a poisonous effect on public support for space exploration if a substantial portion of voters becomes convinced by such theories that space experts, astronauts and scientists are lying to them. Such space tapes are no surprise to NASA; the agency shrugs them off as just one more phenomenon of space flight. The STS-48 images were being collected as part of an ongoing NASA study of unusual lightning. The project was coordinated by NASA scientist Otha "Skeet" Vaughan, in Huntsville, Ala. He has collected and analyzed about 500 hours of tapes over two decades of shuttle flights, probably watching more space video than anyone else. Just Debris Vaughan, who retired from NASA last month, said such dots appear frequently. "They're an ordinary part of space flight," he says. "It's obviously just more shuttle debris." Astronauts aboard the STS-48 mission agree. Mission specialist Mark Brown says ice formed on the shuttle's main engine bells after the remaining fuel was dumped in space. "These crystals would break free of the engines and float around the shuttle," he says. "When illuminated by sunlight they looked like small diamonds floating in space, disturbed only when the maneuvering rockets fired - the plumes from the rockets would hit them and send them off in different directions." Shuttle co-pilot Ken Reightler says: "We saw a lot of this on STS-48 because we had a dump nozzle that was leaking." The same nozzle leaked on the shuttle's next mission and "created the same shower of ice particles - but this time apparently no one misinterpreted them as UFOs." [*Space shuttles are often surrounded by clouds of small ice particles from dumped water or leaking jet thrusters. 'Fireflies' Small particles flaking off manned spacecraft have been around since John Glenn saw "fireflies" outside his capsule in 1962. Apollo astronauts saw them so often they were nicknamed "moon pigeons." A NASA study in 1971 traced them to propellant leaks, water dumps, pyrotechnic separation and other ordinary events. Yet claims for an extraordinary interpretation of the STS-48 images persist, coming from respectable and seemingly rational people. Jack Kasher, a physicist from Nebraska, has published an exhaustive analysis showing why they cannot be debris. "The only feasible explanation," he concludes, "is that they actually were spacecraft out in space away from the shuttle." Mark Carlotto, an imaging specialist in Massachusetts, published a 1995 report in the Journal of Scientific Exploration, claiming that "beyond a reasonable doubt" the objects could not be explained as known phenomena. Shedding Light Two factors - sunlight and the steering-jet pulses - explain the videotape. The shuttle TV cameras observed lightning on the night side of Earth. But as the shuttle circled toward the day side, it rose into sunlight even while the camera remained fixed on the still-dark horizon behind it. So objects near the shuttle suddenly become illuminated - and it's precisely at sunrise that the most famous "shuttle UFO videos" show the appearance of these dots. The autopilot normally fires the shuttle's steering jets to keep the craft on course. Telemetry readouts from STS-48 show exactly such a jet firing at the time of the mystery pulse. Space junk and thruster gas are a lot less exciting than alien visitors and space battles, so the popularity of UFO explanations for such videotapes will persist. But if recent studies prove anything, it is that the less one knows about space flight, the more likely one is to swallow the idea of space shuttles spotting UFOs.

Because Martyn Stubbs wanted to play chess with James Oberg on this new footage, I decided to write to James Oberg by e-mail. Martyn was too ill to make the moves himself so I made the contacts. I told Oberg about the footage and the mission numbers in the following letter to him:

Dear Mr. Oberg, I have NASA video footage never seen by the public before. It reveals an incident which I believe puts NASA in a checkmate position as a follow-up to Jack Kasher's alleged UFO phenomenon. NASA has discredited his alleged UFOs as "dust bunnies" or "Ice crystals." I have an incident, I will not tell you which mission yet, where the shuttle cameras are 100 nautical miles away from a satellite and we see measurable (because we know the size of the satellite) objects passing behind the satellite. Because the satellite is so far away from the cameras and shuttle, and the giant round circles which pulse with energy waves and have obvious architecture, pass behind the satellite, they cannot be "dust bunnies" or ice crystals. They measure 2-3 miles in diameter each and there are over fifty of them surrounding the satellite. I am producing a documentary film about these incidents caught on tape. If you would be interested in seeing the footage and defending NASA's opinions for the film, how would I contact you?

He wrote me back almost immediately the following letter on

November 22, 1999:

I am always happy to look at new claims for anomalous phenomena on shuttle videos. After all, there someday could be real ones. And you will have to identify the source of your tape, by mission and – as best you can – by time, so I can verify that somebody has not digitally altered the original contents, which happens from time to time.

After all, when playing chess, the position of all your pieces is known to your adversary. Or are you playing poker? Speaking of poker, let me call your bluff: where's your proof that NASA ever called Jack Kasher's dots "dust bunnies"? I suggest you have just made this up and that it is not true. If you are expecting me to believe it, or that's what you say can be relied on to be true, I need some proof (that's what makes me rather unpopular among many UFO buffs).

Frankly, I'm astonished that you can believe an object can be seen to pass behind a satellite 100 nautical miles away, since satellites are so small at that range – one pixel on the CCTV – that it is physically impossible to detect whether something passes behind it. But perhaps you are relying on other than visual information.

I didn't give James Oberg all the information for good reason. I didn't tell him which mission and which satellite because I was nervous about exposing this very sensitive mission number. If NASA found out that our group had the tape, they might come after us. But I had to remain fearless if I was going to know the truth. I wrote him back and told him which mission I was talking about: STS-75, February 25, 1996. He wrote me back the following letter on November 24, 1999:

I'd be happy to see your video of the STS-75 mission, but if you just give me the times in the flight you are interested in, I can order my own copies from NASA. Considering the size of the satellite at 20 kilometers, and the thinness of the tether, the basis of your certitude that the objects passed behind rather than in front puzzles me.

James Oberg was certain he could order the tape from NASA so he could see for himself. I had already found many secure documents about this mission on NASA's website that no one could enter without a security code. Why all the secrecy at NASA about this incident? There had to be a just reason to cover it up. As NASA's Space Act signed on July 29, 1958, section 102 (c) (a), we read: "Information obtained or developed by the Administrator in the performance of his functions under this act shall be available for public inspection except: a) information authorized or required by Federal statute to be withheld, and b) information classified to protect the national security." I believed that this was the reason that NASA classified certain documents about STS-75. There was something that happened on that mission caught on tape that revealed such a threat to national security.

James Oberg could not get his own copy of the STS-75 from NASA. There was a block on this mission. I decided to tease him by e-mailing him a still-photo of the tether and the alleged UFOs that I found on NASA's website. The photo shows the UFOs and the tether "before" the NASA cameras zoom in to get a closer look at the objects. It is not a motion picture so it is still hard to tell.

James Oberg went from trying to seduce me with his interest in UFOs to the same devil's advocate the astronaut Edgar Mitchell became. He wrote me on December 2, 1999:

I see normal junk, but to determine if they pass behind the tether, I'll have to look at the video. The tether was sunlit during those videos, there's no need to conjure up imaginative mechanisms of illumination. Heck, I saw it from the ground several times predawn as it orbited hundreds of miles above. I even saw it come out of the Earth's shadow and "appear" just as it became sunlit. Where's the mystery?

I wrote him and asked him if he got a copy of the video from NASA. He wrote me back on December 3, 1999:

No, it's way down on my priority list. I don't expect to get to it for some time. If you can dub a tape, I'll pay reasonable expenses ($20 or so) for a copy.

If it was so far down on his priority list, why did he write me immediately following my letters to him? Why did he ask me for a copy of the tape unless he couldn't get his own from NASA as he said he could? I told him Martyn Stubbs would send him a tape and I gave Martyn James Oberg's address.

Martyn Stubbs was claiming to be very ill from his brain tumor. He was so sick that he could not get out of bed. I didn't have another copy of the tape to send to James Oberg and thought Martyn would. Martyn didn't send him a tape. Perhaps he was scared of being interrogated by NASA.

If NASA sequestered this mission's footage in its archives "for eyes only," then were our lives in real danger of being interrogated by the NSA? Perhaps that is why Martyn didn't give James Oberg the tape just yet.

Martyn may be dying of this tumor that some might suspect was an attack on him by the NSA. Mike Boyle and I thought we might be next. I didn't care. I still struggled and wanted to know the truth regardless of death threats that still were not imminent to me right now.

James Oberg kept writing me and asking for the video. We never sent it to him. He would have to be patient and wait. I could already see that no matter how obvious it was on the tape that the UFOs were passing "behind" the tether confirming their size and confirming them to be UFOs, James Oberg would do the same thing anyone working for NASA would do: come up with some fancy physics to try and explain how light was causing a magical illusion. Our research group was in no hurry to let him kill us over dinner.

If you want to know the truth from a lion you have to go into the lion's den for dinner. I would now go further into NASA than I already had.

III – Contacting Dr. Louis A. Frank at NASA

In November of 1999, I finally made contact with Dr. Louis A. Frank at NASA. He was the one who Dr. Joseph Nuth, III at NASA wrote me about that discovered these mysterious objects on the "DE

spacecraft's UV cameras." I sent him a letter describing the contents of the videotape as follows:

Dear Dr. Frank,

I have what may be a surprise for you. I formed a partnership with a man in Vancouver, B.C. named Martyn Stubbs who, as Program Manager of a Cable TV station there, recorded over 400 hours of 1990s NASA space shuttle missions. He began to notice numerous astounding incidents where Unidentified Objects appeared. He then scrutinized the 400 hours of footage and began to discover the Unidentified Objects showed signs of intelligence (gathering in formations of triangles and circles), defied the laws of gravity (escaping earth) and motion (make sudden directional changes) for known natural objects in the solar system, etc. All of this you can see on the enclosed 7-minute sample videotape.

Filmed during the STS75 Mission in February, 1996, was the most astounding event captured on film and broadcast to the word by NASA ever. It revealed a swarm of over 50 of these Unidentified Objects surrounding and passing by the Satellite and 12-mile tether (conductor cable experiment). Sample this incident on the enclosed video.

The NASA cameras zoom in for the first time to get a clear look at these objects to reveal their clear circular shape with obvious portals (architecture) and relative size as they pass behind the satellite/tether which are 77-100 nautical miles away from the space shuttle/cameras. This first reveals that the circular objects reveal their relative size against the 12-mile long tether (a perfect measuring rod in space).

If an object passes behind another measurable object in space, the object can be measured at a minimum relative size to the measurable object for reasons that are obvious to you. These Unidentified Objects measure at a minimum (they are larger depending on how far they are behind the tether) 2-3 miles in diameter against the 12-mile satellite/tether. This is astounding!

You can also calculate their speed of travel along the 12-mile tether: some over 35,000 mph!

When similar NASA video footage revealing small, Unidentified Objects was brought forward to the public audience of the world (Dr. Jack Kasher), NASA called the objects "dust bunnies" in front of the video camera lens or near shuttle environment. This piece of footage eliminates that hypothesis because the Unidentified Objects pass behind the satellite/tether, which are 77-100 nautical miles away from the cameras. The objects are much too large to be "dust bunnies."

I have enclosed here for you a 7-minute sample video of the phenomenon mentioned. It shows just a small fraction of the whole incidents (in our possession) mentioned in the enclosed screenplay for documentary "Evidence 2001."

I have 7 letters from Dr. Joseph Nuth, III, Head of NASA Astrochmistry Branch, which mention you and your findings with Polaris. As Dr. Nuth describes your mystery objects as "house-sized and fluffy," and I have seen many objects over Martynn Stubbs' NASA video with the same physical characteristics, I think we are looking at the same objects. I have therefore contacted you for your possible interest in being interviewed for this film. If you read the enclosed screenplay and appendices, you will see the very scientific investigative approach I am intending for this subject matter.

I am raising funds for the documentary now. If you would be interested in being interviewed as mentioned in the screenplay, please write me a letter of your interest soon.

Also, upon your possible interest in this project, I would be happy to share the incidents you saw on the 7-minute sample tape in their complete length as well as many other incidents

Martyn Stubbs has in his NASA video collection. I hope to hear from you soon. Happy New Millennium!

Dr. Louis A. Frank is Carver/James A. Van Allen Professor of Physics at the University of Iowa, where he has been a member f the faculty since 1964. His first professional research activities occurred in 1958 when he assisted professor Van Allen in the calibration of the first U.S. lunar probes, Pioneers 3 and 4, as an undergraduate student. Since then he has been an experimenter, co-investigator, or principal investigator for instruments aboard forty-two spacecraft. The types of instrumentation include those for energetic charged particles, plasmas, and auroral imaging. He has been, or currently is, the principal investigator for plasma instruments on fourteen spacecraft, including Quadrispherical LEPEDEAs on two International Sun-Earth Explorers (ISEEs) and several Interplanetary Monitoring Platforms (IMPs). Dr. Frank is the principal investigator for the auroral imaging instruments for the Dynamics Explorer Mission, the plasma instrumentation for the Galileo Mission to Jupiter, the U.S. plasma instrumentation for the Japanese Geotail spacecraft, and the camera for visible wavelengths for the Polar spacecraft of the International Solar Terrestrial Physics (ISTP) Program.

He has served on various NASA and NAS/NRC committees and is Fellow of the American Physical Society, a member of the American Astronomical Society, American Association for the Advancement of Science and the International Academy of Astronautics. He is Fellow of the American Geophysical Union and a recipient of the National Space Act Award.

Within one week, I received a Federal Express envelope from Dr. Frank. The package was filled with scientific data on his discoveries at NASA for my perusal. He was obviously excited about the tape, I thought. The data in this package was enough to keep me busy for months.

What I was looking for was possible confirmation that Dr. Louis A. Dr. Frank's discovery of what Dr. Joseph Nuth, III at NASA called "SOMETHING" (not comets) was, according to Dr. Frank, actually a very new discovery in the solar system: small comets made mostly of water. In a pamphlet he sent me titled "Small Comets and Our Origins: The Ecstasy and Agony of the Scientific Debate," a Sixteenth Annual

Presidential Lecture at The University of Iowa, Iowa City, Iowa, a quotation from Kathy Sawyer stated, "It is a shocking notion. Radiation-blasted, black-jacketed snowballs the size of houses swarming out of the cosmic void every day plowing into Earth's atmosphere and pancaking explosively into clouds of vapor that fall as gentle rains. Over billions of years these invaders might have filled Earth's oceans and provided the seeds of life."

It seemed that Dr. Frank and his researchers believed that water balls the size of small houses were being identified by the NASA Polaris Satellite. It was also clear in the title of this pamphlet that this subject was the center of a heated debate at NASA. I knew what the heart of that debate entailed: As Dr. Nuth wrote me in the beginning of my investigation, "You have enumerated a few of the problems with Frank's hypothesis and probably now realize why few scientists think the phenomena seen by Lou Frank are actually comets. No one doubts that he has observed SOMETHING, just not comets." The heart of the impossible physics for Dr. Frank's hypothesis are because water simply could not have survived the intense radiation from stars and the sun while the water was in transit from one point in the solar system to arrive at Earth. Also, Dr. Nuth noted that if these were actually water, the solar radiation would produce a noticeable infrared signal (sun interacting with water) and no signal was observed on infrared or ever has been.

Dr. Frank's data includes the fact that there are over 10 million of these alleged water comets impacting Earth's atmosphere each year. He deduces that, at this rate over the age of the earth, the small comets can provide enough water to fill our oceans with water. Frank's data implies that an incoming "small comet" made of water is approximately 40 feet in diameter. It then breaks up while 800 miles above the earth and then vaporizes into a water cloud 30 miles in diameter while 330 miles above the Earth. His theory sounds remarkable and appears to deserve a major investigation at NASA and it has.

Dr. Joseph Nuth wrote to me a powerful reason against the theory that these objects cold be made of water:

I'd suggest that you count the number of objects between the earth and the shuttle (assume and altitude of ~300 mi.), use to calculate a "space density" for these objects. Multiply this space density by the mass of the objects to figure the influx of material to the surface of the Earth. Or, use this density to figure the time for the shuttle or an average satellite to be struck by one of these objects. Not only is the mass flux much too high to ignore, but no satellite has a chance in surviving days, let alone years if these were actually meteors."

It is a compelling statement from Dr. Nuth that, considering 10 million of these impactors, at 40 tons each, travelling some 35,000 miles per hour, that they would pose the most serious threat to satellites and perhaps even the space shuttle itself. Imagine the shuttle getting hit by a 40-ton ball of water doing 35,000 mph. What would happen? It would destroy the shuttle or any satellite. Because that has not happened, Dr. Nuth does not believe these objects are made of water. Again, what then are they?

How does Dr. Frank discover that these large objects are made of water? According to his data, Dr. Frank shows that the NASA Polaris satellite detected "oxygen trails" that produce luminous trails caused by "resonantly scattered radiation from atomic oxygen exposed to solar radiation." This shows that he did not actually find water and actual comets, rather the NASA Polaris satellite detected "atomic oxygen" which becomes luminous when it is exposed to intense solar radiation.

It is an "assumption" of his that the oxygen is produced when the water (H_2O) in the small comets is broken down by the radiation from the sun: at 1,700 degrees f, hydrogen separates from oxygen. There is no clear evidence that there is water anywhere.

There is only clear evidence that there is oxygen trails becoming luminous when undergoing nuclear reactions under the influence of solar radiation. When oxygen (O_2) is bombarded by solar radiation, a nuclear reaction is caused that turns oxygen into ozone (O_3) . That means there should be some heat present caused by this reaction. Heat should be detected by infrared satellites, and as Dr. Joseph Nuth, III, Head of NASA Astrochemistry stated in the previously mentioned letter to me, "These fluffy, house-sized objects should have been at a temperature near 300k or even higher…. they should therefore be infrared beacons. Yet no other satellite has ever seen evidence for these objects. This includes a vast array of Department of Defense satellites as well as far as I can learn."

There is a great mystery going on here. Either NASA is not providing Dr. Frank with real data that these oxygen trails are showing up on other satellites and possibly on space shuttle missions, or the luminous, alleged oxygen trails are unfounded. Something else would have to be causing the luminous effect. The other possibility is that the cause of this luminous effect is an energy source absorbing radiation in the ultraviolet range of the light energy spectrum. This energy source may be an unknown phenomena all together and may have nothing to do with water.

But Dr. Louis A. Frank shows clear data and evidence that 20-40 ton water balls are hitting the Earth's upper atmosphere at a rate of 10-20 million per year. He is actually seeing them dissolving into water clouds and then vaporizing. From his data we can see the evidence:

Of interest for the present discussion are the facts that (1) the atmospheric holes (small comets) expand to maximum diameters of 100 kilometers, (2) the expansion rate of the diameters is about 1 kilometer per second, (3) the lifetime of the atmospheric holes is about 100 seconds, (4) the apparent speeds are in the range of 0 to 20 kilometers per second.

This data shows astounding evidence of an object impacting the upper atmosphere of Earth and then expanding upon impact and then dissolving all together in 100 seconds. The dissolving rate is of the most interest to me. If such comets of water dissolve so quickly upon entering the Earth's atmosphere and under the influence of cosmic and solar radiation, how could they have traveled from deep space to Earth without also dissolving? This is the heart of the debate at NASA against this discovery.

If Dr. Frank is right and Dr. Nuth is right, then the hypothesis gets more interesting. If these 40-ton balls of water are hitting Earth's upper atmosphere at a rate of 10 million per year, and they are not hitting any of our satellites or the space shuttle, my own hypothesis suggests that they must be intelligently directed away from such targets. Also, considering that it is impossible for water to survive the transit from one point in space to arrive at Earth due to intense solar radiation, then something must have transported the water to Earth by intelligent means. The only intelligent reason I can hypothesize for an extraterrestrial civilization to be dumping water or oxygen on top of Earth's atmosphere is because oxygen transmutates into ozone.

We all know that Earth's ozone layer is dying. What if an intelligent race of extraterrestrials was trying to help us heal our ozone layer? It is the only theory that makes sense as to explain why the water balls are not hitting any of our satellites and destroying them. Also, this new theory can explain how the water survived a transit in space without being destroyed by solar radiation. Another hypothesis is that the large UFOs are invisible because they are in the UV range of light and that they are scooping up water from our own oceans and dumping it on our atmosphere to heal our ozone layer.

If we go through more of Dr. Frank's data, we can see how my own hypothesis gets stronger.

Dr. Frank's data revealed also how the NASA Dynamics Explorer 1 satellite detected these "small comets" in the ultraviolet spectrum of light energy:

Transient decreases of Earth's far-ultraviolet dayglow were first detected with a spin-scan imager on board the Dynamics Explorer 1 spacecraft was launched into an eccentric polar orbit for global views of the auroral zones and dayglow. The diameters of these transient decreases, or atmospheric holes, were in the range of 50 to 100 km, and their durations were about 100 seconds. Because the dimensions of the atmospheric holes were large, this phenomenon was interpreted as water vapor clouds from small comets which were disrupted and vaporized by sunlight above the upper atmosphere. Water vapor is an efficient absorber of the far-ultraviolet emissions, primarily those from atomic oxygen at 130.4 and 130.6 nm. From the upper atmosphere.

Again he even admits here that the "comets were vaporized by sunlight above the upper atmosphere. So how could the water comets have survived transit in deep space to Earth without vaporizing in the few seconds that it takes for water to vaporize under solar radiation? In his examples, the 40-ton water balls vaporize in 100 seconds. How then did they survive any longer while in deep space transit to Earth? It is impossible.

I had sent Dr. Frank a full, second copy of the NASA alleged UFO video for his own investigation. I also wanted to see if we were seeing some of the same phenomenon, meaning the "small comets" that he discovered and the balls of light flying by on the NASA UFO video. I wrote him another letter with the following list of questions for him:

NEW QUESTIONS FOR DR. LOUIS A. FRANK

1. I feel there are too many similarities to your observations of "small comets" detected using the UV camera on Polaris with those characteristics of the unidentified flying objects seen on the NASA videotape. Dr. Joseph Nuth, III, NASA Head of Astrochemistry described your phenomenon as "fluffy, house-sized objects of low density." Many of the unidentified objects that appear on the NASA videotapes fit these same characteristics: fluffy, house-sized, low density (some appear ghost-like). You even found that your phenomenon leave "atomic oxygen trails," which, when exposed to solar radiation, produce "scattering of radiation" leaving the appearance of a luminous trail. The same phenomenon appears in the NASA video when we see these unidentified flying objects: the luminous trails.

2. The very first question I asked Dr. Nuth was that "If these little meteors are hitting the earth's upper atmosphere (and as you detected water), wouldn't the intense solar radiation separate the H20 into Oxygen and Hydrogen; thus releasing tremendous amounts of oxygen into the upper atmosphere. When oxygen undergoes further solar radiation, O2 transmutates into O3 (Ozone). Could these space meteorites be healing our ozone layer?" While Dr. Nuth didn't think there were enough of these "small comets" (as you call them) to make a substantial difference, what does your research show (you detect 10 -20 million 40 ton water comets per year)? Could these miraculous "small comets" have seeded earth with water, hydrogen and oxygen to co-create our atmosphere?

3. You eliminate the possibility that your "small comets" are dust balls by this same analysis: that oxygen is being released by the "small comets" and, further reacting under solar radiation, producing visible trails. Of course a dust ball could not produce oxygen under the influence of solar radiation. I see then how you deduced that there must be a presence of water: Oxygen & Hydrogen.

4. As NASA has tried to discredit some of the phenomenon seen on the NASA videos as "dust bunnies," (Even Dr. Nuth), could you apply the same analysis of luminous trails seen on the video to "oxygen trails" and eliminate the NASA "dust bunny" hypothesis on that fact alone?

5. It is very curious to me that, if the top of the earth's atmosphere is 100 miles (Dr. Nuth's data), and the space shuttle is at 300 miles, and supposed meteors are going by which have bright trails (see Video of MIR sequence), meteors could not flare and produce a visible trail unless they were actually striking earth's atmosphere (200 miles below the altitude of the space shuttle). Again, the only way a meteor could flare at such a high altitude would be if it were releasing oxygen or hydrogen and producing what you call "scattered radiation." That again leaves us with the possibility that we are seeing the same objects: NASA video unidentified objects and your "small comets."

6. Does the fact that your "small comets" only show up on UV (and not infra-red), as light is energy, and UV light is more energetic than visible and infra-red, suggest that these 'small comets" are radiating with actual energy? If so, how energetic are they and where does this energy they radiate come from? Could water, exposed to intense solar radiation, produce the far UV signal (perhaps solar radiation of hydrogen and oxygen)? Have measurements been taken in near, far and extreme UV, x-rays and gamma spectrums? Do your "small comets only show up in the far UV range, eliminating the others?

7. Have you seen any supporting data from other UV cameras on satellites such as: 1. Orfeus-Spas II, Astro 1 and 2 or The International Ultraviolet Explorer? Certainly Orfeus-Spas II, if focused where Polaris is focused, should have even better results, as it is the latest and most advanced UV camera? Do you know the Principal Investigator(s) for Orfeus Spas II?

8. When you hypothesize that your "small comets" release atomic

oxygen (by solar radiation of water which should produce hydrogen as well?) which reacts with solar radiation further to produce "resonantly scattered radiation (atomic oxygen trails)," you reveal that there must be some heat (energy) produced by this reaction. Therefore, shouldn't this heat produce an infra-red signal? Dr. Nuth deducts that this should produce a temperature of 300k or even higher. If so, why did Dr. Nuth tell me that no infra-red satellite camera has ever seen evidence of your "small comets?" This included, he wrote, "COBE, IRAS, ISO and a vast array of DoD satellites?"

9. Although there are many similar characteristics to the unidentified flying objects seen on the NASA video to your "small comets," there are considerable differences as well:

a) Many times on the NASA video we see these balls of light travelling much slower than 10-20 km/s, sometimes they nearly stop altogether. How could a comet move so slowly under the influence of earth's gravity? While Dr. Nuth, III wrote that "most meteors have velocities greater than 20 km/s – some travel slower," how could a small comet or meteor nearly stop and travel so slow as many of the unidentified objects do in the NASA video?

b) There is one scene on the tape I sent you where we see a brightly glowing object with a long trail leaving the earth's atmosphere: impossible for a comet or meteor or even space junk, unless the brightly glowing object had energy to escape gravity. That is why I asked you in question 4 if UV energy, being more radiant than visible light energy, qualified these "small comets" as potential energy sources or should I dare suggest "plasma energy sources?" The implications to this hypothesis are far reaching, in that (I am going out on a limb here) these proposed "plasma energy sources" may hold the answer to nuclear fusion, advanced physics and intelligent life.

c) In the STS-75 "Tether Incident" – well documented in the screenplay – we can see for the first time, the space shuttle's B&W cameras zoom in and we get a clearer look at the unidentified flying objects actual architecture and structure: circular with obvious portals and pulse/waves of energy, yet appear low in density.

d) Could these be a form of living plasma (water, gas and ?) but with a phenomenal membrane to protect it from intense solar and stellar radiation? Could the released oxygen which produces the "atomic

137

oxygen trail" be released as a byproduct of their own inner nuclear reactions? Watch on the video how one of them pulses, it seems, with energy. What do you observe here?

e) Also, in the "Tether incident" the unidentified flying objects can be measured against the 12-mile long tether as they clearly pass behind it. I come up with 2-3 miles in diameter for the largest ones as a minimum size, depending on how far the objects are passing behind the tethered satellite. If they are farther in distance behind the tethered satellite than I suspect, they could be even larger. This is the only piece of video where I can measure size and distances as NASA has provided all of this information during the broadcast. This gives us sizes that are much grater than "house-sized small comets." Comments?

f) During the "tether incident" close-ups of the unidentified flying objects, we can see clear architecture and structure revealing that they do not appear amorphous and rugged in shape as I understand comets, meteors or shooting stars would. Rather, they appear intelligently structured as a living thing, something one would observe under a microscope, or perhaps intelligent-living-plasma-energy-bodies from another civilization, or perhaps "living critters" as astronaut Scott Carpenter described as "I have the fireflies" which surrounded his Mercury 7 spacecraft. What do you think when you see this on the NASA videotape?

g) On the video I sent you, you can see the formation of a semi-circle over the continent of Africa. I believe this shows intelligence as a gathering of sorts for intelligent beings who wish to congregate towards one another, something one would not expect for any natural object in the solar system to do. Can you hypothesize further on this incident?

h) If we are looking at the same objects, the question of their possible "intelligence" brings one more question: Why don't Mars and Venus have oceans and atmospheres? As this phenomenon of water comets should be a common solar system member, shouldn't these water comets be depositing the ingredients for water on Mars and Venus? If those two planets and others are not being bombarded by your proposed water comets, then could we suggest that they have intelligently been sent to earth to co-create our oceans, lakes and very atmosphere? If you hypothesize no actual intelligence, then how did they obviate the other planets?

In response to my long list of questions, Dr. Frank wrote me the following letter by e-mail on December 12, 1999:

Dear David, I have received your second video and letter dated 2 December 1999. I find the contents of both videos fascinating. There are several objects, which may be small comets in the videos. Other phenomenon being recorded in the videos are not easily explained. Several of us have examined the videos many times. I am very interested in speaking with you on the phone concerning the contents of the videos. This coming week I have to be at a large conference in San Francisco to present papers on other matters. When I return, I will contact you.

This was an exciting letter from a scientist of such highly esteemed education. The very fact that he believes that some of the objects on the video (mostly streaking objects) may be his "small comets" would confirm that, for one, the space shuttle's low light level black & white cameras were seeing into the ultraviolet light range (invisible to the human eye). Also, this would confirm that, either the other departments at NASA were not sharing any of this information with him, or that they were deliberately avoiding sharing this information with him. Because Dr. Frank was only seeing his "small comets" on still-camera pictures previous to his seeing the NASA video, he now had new evidence to work with to support his theories: other cameras were seeing the "small comets."

But there was another amazing observation I had about this letter and that was that people at NASA don't come out in the open and admit that they can't explain the phenomenon on this tape. They either try to easily explain some fabricated lie to ease the public perception or they don't say anything at all when they know they are in trouble. He and his researchers had watched the video several times. They must have been as amazed as I was about it. If it were merely dust, they wouldn't have watched it more than once. Yet, he said that, "Other phenomenon being recorded in the videos are not easily explained."

Dr. Frank can eliminate dust particles being observed on camera by his amazing understanding of light waves as stated in his research paper, "Detection of atomic oxygen trails of small comets in the vicinity of Earth."

Here we can see his studies of the movements of small comets and their streaking oxygen trails distinguishing them from stars and even debris in the vicinity of the satellite:

> The apparent angular widths of the trails (caused by small comets) are generally less than the angular resolution of the earth camera, about two pixels or o.16 degrees. However, the width of the trail at maximum intensities in figure 2 begins to exceed this width. This is demonstrated by the normalized responses shown in figure 4 for the trail of a star. There is no star in the field-of-view in figure 1. The selected star is taken from the same orbit. The width of the trail is estimated to be about 3 pixels or 0.24 degrees. The apparent angular speed for the brighter trail presented here in figures 1 and 2 is about 0.24 degrees per second and that for the dimmer trail in figure 3 is about 0.11 degrees per second. With the assumption that the present objects are part of the small comet distribution is observed at altitudes of < 3000 km as atmospheric holes and as trails in the emissions from the radical OH then their apparent speeds are typically 10 kilometers per second.

Of particular interest to the NASA UFO investigation is the following statement made in the same paper:

> The above findings severely constrain the interpretation of light curves. First of all the uniformity of the light curves eliminates the possibility of debris in the vicinity of the spacecraft.

Could Dr. Frank solve the NASA UFO problem just by studying their light curves? It seemed he could. His paper continues:

> Secondly, the emissions are detected for a brief period, about 15 to 20 seconds. We interpret these intensities as rising over a period of about 15 seconds and decaying within 2 or 3 seconds. Of course, the light curve can be interpreted as rising in 2 or 3 seconds and decaying in 15 seconds. In any case, the event is impulsive with time scales of tens of seconds.
> Two plausible possibilities remain for the interpretation of these

transient events, an exploding comet or an exploding dust ball. If the far-ultraviolet responses to the Earth Camera are due to reflectance of the solar radiation from dust then the brightness of the trail at visible wavelengths should be in the range of about 4,000 kiloRayleighs (kr) within the passbands of the Low-Resolution Visible Camera. For example, an uppper limit of about 0.5 kr is found within the passband at 557.7 nm. Thus the trails are not due to dust.

I thought that if Dr. frank could eliminate the same dust theory as a possible cause to his observations on small comets using this kind of light curve physics, he could do the same to the NASA UFOs. NASA had always tried to tell the public that the alleged UFOs were just pieces of dust and space debris. It was all too obvious that these giant circular objects were not pieces of dust, let alone the other compelling scenes.

Again, considering the qualifications and practical experience in dealing with space phenomenon of Dr. Louis A. Frank, for him to admit that the "Other phenomenon being recorded in the video are not easily explained" was as good of an answer as I was going to get from NASA at this time. He knew I couldn't be fooled by cheap physics. He had to either be as astounded as I was, or he would have to come up with a theory that I could not argue. While the months passed, I didn't get any answers, nor did I have any of my phone calls to him answered.

While I anticipated a deep answer from Dr. Louis A. Frank and his phone call, I received neither by March of 2000. I received one e-mail that mentioned that he had been ill with the flu and had not been able to finish his research into the video yet and that he would get back to me. Perhaps I just needed to be patient.

Chapter Six
Quantum Physics of the NASA UFOs

"A new scientific truth does not triumph by convincing its opponents and making them see the light, but rather because its opponents eventually die and a new generation grows up that is familiar with it"
- Max Planck

I – Baffled by Quantum Physics?

Why was this investigation on the NASA alleged UFOs moving into quantum physics? Because without some basic understanding of magnetism, gravity and light integrated into quantum ideas, the next observations about the UFOs would be impossible to comprehend. We were about to study phenomena that only quantum physics could explain.

On the night of January 10, 2000, a giant new theory in quantum physics exploded into my mind with crystal clarity. The theory would prove that gravity is gradient in frequencies that eventually, at a higher frequency, would go so far beyond light speed, and that those higher frequencies of gravity could conquer the vast diameter of our own galaxy (100,000 light years) in one second and then in zero time. Eventually the theory would show how the highest frequencies of gravity could conquer the distance of the entire universe in zero time, thus gravity at this highest frequency would be the only force that is truly beyond time and space.

Before I present this new theory, I will first need to summarize a few observations in quantum physics, a brief history of electromagnetism, wave theory and particle theory in quantum physics.

Quantum physicists are truly baffled by the observation that electrons exhibit when they absorb photons. Electrons disappear from one orbiting radius position around the proton in an atom and reappear at a higher fixed energy level (closer to the center) without appearing to pass through the interval of space between. These are called "electron shifts." They make a quantum jump from one point in subatomic space and time to another without there being any detectable proof that these electrons passed through the intervening space. This strange behavior of electrons has been well recorded. Physicists call this leap "quantum" because it is such a giant leap and there appears to be no space and time that the electron had to pass through to get from point "a" to point "b." How then did they do it? No one knows for certain.

While many physicists claim that no one has observed the same phenomenon in astronomy and outer space, Dr. William G. Tift, a University of Arizona astronomer found evidence of such a phenomenon in deep space. He calls the phenomena "red shifts," which are very much like "electron shifts." The shifts in the spectra of light coming from distant galaxies are grouped in abrupt, regular steps, not a smoothly random distribution that one would expect to find in physics theories of relativity. The observations were called "heretical" by most scientists and dismissed as a mistake. Dr. Tift didn't think so. After all, he was the one doing the research.

It was as if galaxies could travel from only at specific speeds, jumping abruptly from one speed to another, without passing through the intermediary speeds. This seemed impossible to conventional physicists. The phenomenon was also all too similar to "electron shifts." Suddenly, the micro-universe phenomenon was being witnessed in the macro-universe by astronomers.

Dr. Tift, an astronomer at the University of Arizona, does not claim to understand the effect. No one does. It has been observed but no one can understand the physics of such a movement. But he believes the quantized red-shifting, seemingly analogous to the abrupt jumps between energy levels that nuclear particles undergo, might one day explain the force of gravity in terms of quantum theory, a goal long sought after by theoretical physicists.

Tift has been presenting data on this for a decade now. He said, "It's always been impossible, and that's why there's such an incredible surprise. The periodicity number seems to come up all the time, and I don't have an explanation. If it's true, then we know less than we think."

Dr. Tift and Dr. Cocke strongly agree with that assessment. In an article in the magazine Sky & Telescope, they wrote that the advent of quantum theory at the start of the 20th century turned classical physics on its ear. They added, "As the turn of the next century approaches, we again find an established science in trouble trying to explain the behavior of the natural world."

Most astronomers have ignored Tift's claims because of their inherent implausibility. It should be duly noted that "inherent implausibility" is believed by most astrophysicists to be true because no existing theory in physics and astrophysics can explain the great mystery of gravity.

Dr. John P. Huchra of the Harvard-Smithsonian Center For Astrophysics said, "I've personally decided that I'm not going to spend much time working on that problem. I don't see its connection to the physical model that we understand at the moment. And I'm not sure it's correct."

But Dr. Huchra added, "On the other hand, there have been some high precision radio telescope observations of spiral galaxies, and there have been a few papers that seem to back Tift up. So I'm a fence sitter." Dr. Tift believes his fresh evidence that the conventional explanation of red shifts must be reassessed, but so far there has been no theory to explain them.

This is the key point that I am trying to make, that "no existing theory" in physics and astrophysics can explain gravity in gradient frequencies that eventually go beyond light speed.

Before I will explain gravity beyond light speed theory to answer "electron shifts," "red shifts" and even UFOs making hyper-dimensional jumps through space and time in the same manner, we will examine a brief history of electromagnetic fields, gravity, physics and quantum physics.

Michael Faraday

Michael Faraday was from England. There he discovered that an electrical current could produce a magnetic field. He, in fact, invented the term "magnetic field." He also constructed a device that was the predecessor to the modern electromagnetic generators first designed by Nikola Tesla. Faraday found that by rotating a bar magnet in the vicinity of a current-carrying wire, he showed that the magnetic field could "induce" the current that would flow through the wire, thus electricity. In other words, he found that the moving magnet could generate an electrical current in a wire. This major discovery made it possible to turn magnetism into electricity as well as electricity into magnetism. It suggests that electricity and magnetism can be interchanged, and that this interchange, called electromagnetism, led to the theoretical discovery of electromagnetic waves led by Maxwell and Hertz.

Clerk Maxwell

By 1860, the idea of electromagnetism was accepted. James Clerk Maxwell, also from England, had discovered, through his interpretation of Faraday's work, that the process of turning electricity into magnetism and magnetism back into electricity could be repeated over and over, very quickly in the form of electrical oscillations. These oscillations were, however, only a theory of his at this point in time. They were predicted to occur only on paper. The question was: could they be observed? What would they look like?

Maxwell meditated on this great mystery for a long time. It occurred to him that light waves previously discovered by another scientist named Young may be produced by electromagnetic oscillations. By playing with his equations, he found an astonishing fact: the equations describing the electromagnetic vibrations had solutions that described electromagnetic waves moving at the speed of light. Could light waves just be one frequency of electromagnetic oscillations, thus a frequency of gravity?

Maxwell's successful attempt to show that electromagnetic/ gravity waves were theoretically able to travel at the speed of light compared to Young's experimental discovery that light could interfere with itself was convincing evidence to Maxwell that light was an

electromagnetic wave, thus a gravity wave vibrating at a particular frequency.

Where would this research evolve to next? What happened in modern physics that caused science to turn away from oscillating wave theory?

Heinrich Hertz

In 1887, James Clerk Maxwell's theories received supporting evidence from the works of Heinrich Hertz. Hertz successfully demonstrated that an electromagnetic wave of invisible radiation was emitted by an oscillating electrical current. Hertz's experiments on the detection and production of electromagnetic waves convinced the scientific world that light and heat must also be frequencies of electromagnetic waves.

All of the spectra of light were just wavelengths of particular frequencies of electromagnetic waves. Frequency refers to how frequently a wave oscillated (completed a circuit) per second. One Hertz was equal to One electromagnetic wave per second. We measure radio waves in Hertz to describe the frequency of the wave.

Today the light spectrum is well understood, as demonstrated in Chapter One – II in this book.

Nikola Tesla

Just six years after Hertz demonstrated his principle that electromagnetic waves were produced by an oscillating electrical current, Tesla demonstrated radio waves and the first form of radio at the Chicago World's fair in 1893, several years before Marconi made his claims and gained world fame. Tesla had invented the "Tesla Coil" which was responsible for allowing engineers to take an electrical current and alter the current into higher and lower frequencies of magnetic waves. These higher frequencies of waves could allow for signals of intelligent information, radio and eventually TV, to be transmitted across the ether without wires. The signals could be received at another end for interpretation. Tesla proved that electromagnetic waves could be produced at different frequencies.

Tesla even produced light by creating a magnetic wave equal to the frequency of light itself. This experiment was Tesla's proof that there were higher or faster than light speed magnetic frequencies in the universe that could be utilized. Tesla's work in this field would have already revolutionized and solved the greatest mysteries in quantum physics had he been understood properly. His papers in physics were published but were not taken seriously.

Max Planck

On December 14, 1900, an articulate forty-two year old professor named Max Planck presented an astounding concept to the August body of the German Physical Society. This date would later be regarded as the birthday of "Quantum Physics."

Planck created a new formula in physics called $E = hf$. It is basically a magnetic frequency of a wave theory. Energy (E) is equal the to frequency (f) of a wave (h), later known as "Planck's Constant." The "h" in his theory became known as Planck's constant because waves were said to be a constant in the universe, just as light energy was discovered by Einstein to be the only true constant speed in the universe. Planck's idea of a constant to a wave was different than what modern physicists believe: he observed that light is only one frequency of a magnetic or gravity wave while there are many other frequencies of waves that have still not yet been measured. The frequency with which each wave oscillated was the "f" in Planck's theory. Tesla's work concurs with this perfectly.

Higher frequency (faster oscillations) meant higher energy. Consequently, higher frequency light could not be seen as it vibrated above the visible light spectrum. This is demonstrated as we examine the relatively longer wavelengths of visible light and the shorter or faster wavelengths of ultraviolet light that vibrate so quickly that they go beyond the highest spectrum of visible light. Because we view phenomena in visible light speed time, our brains and our observation tools cannot see light and energy vibrating faster than the frequency with which our brains can also oscillate. Perhaps this is why Einstein did not believe in faster than light vibrations: the brain could not see them nor could most cameras.

What Max Planck had discovered in theory needed a practical scientific model to prove it. While the spectra of light clearly demonstrates his principle, he needed a working applied model of an electrical operating device to prove it. I am deeply surprised that he never met and studied with Nikola Tesla because the Tesla coil demonstrated this perfectly.

Tesla burned atmospheric nitrogen with high frequency discharges radiating off of his coils and produced 12 million volts of electricity. I checked this fact with Dr. Bogdan Maglich, the nuclear fusion scientist I was an associate of, and he told me that this would have been one of the first nuclear reactions in science and it would have been non-radioactive.

What Max Planck needed was proof that there was higher energy that could be utilized present in higher frequency magnetic waves or electric fields. While Tesla proved it, Max Planck did not recognize Tesla's work and suffered a great loss.

But within his formula $E = hf$, Max Planck started a furor. A new precedent in science, particularly in physics, had been born. There was no independent evidence for Planck's $E = hf$ formula (he missed Tesla) and so the embarrassing thing was that there was no way to prove it. There was no way to see it, visualize it, or even connect it with any other formula.

Because Planck and the rest of the scientific community had no way of applying Planck's discovery to an experiment or machine, his theory was sequestered for a time. He also had no diagrams to clearly indicate what he meant by this.

Using Faraday, Maxwell, Hertz and Tesla and uniting their theories and work into Planck's, we can see a great synthesis: that light energy may be produced by electromagnetic oscillations. By playing

148

with his equations, Planck found an astonishing fact: the equations describing the electromagnetic vibrations had solutions that described electromagnetic waves moving at the speed of light. Light waves could then be described as frequencies of electromagnetic vibrations. If so, light and gravity were just different frequencies of the same kind of electromagnetic waves.

All of this would only prove Nikola Tesla as correct when he demonstrated that gravity waves in the higher ether were vibrating faster than light speed and that by creating a frequency of magnetism (gravity) using his coils, he could attract electromagnetic energy waves and slow them down to the speed of light and he could create light. He did this with success. Tesla proved that gravity was gradient and that it vibrated faster than light in higher frequencies in the ethers.

Albert Einstein

The idea of an ether being filled with waves of energy was foreign to Albert Einstein. He banished that theory in 1905. He believed that space was a true void with nothing in it. Einstein took Max Planck to heart but he eventually rejected the idea that the there was any such thing as an ether vibrating with energy waves or beyond light speed magnetic waves such as Tesla and Planck had believed.

Instead of light waves being magnetic waves, Einstein saw that light was made of mass particles called photons. These photons were made of mass and had energy because they were high velocity particles. This is where Einstein revolutionized Max Planck's $E = hf$ into $E = mc2$. Energy (E) was now equal to the velocity of mass. For instance, the faster electrons (mass) flowed through a current carrying wire, the more energy could be measured. Instead of the frequency of magnetic waves being related to energy, energy was now related to the velocity of mass.

Today, both Planck and Einstein's ideas can be merged as physicists now believe in both wave and particle theories. According to Planck's $E = hf$, the energy of each bit of mass somehow had to be dependent on the frequency of the light wave which mass was moving through or influenced by.

Einstein won the Nobel Prize in Physics in 1921 for explaining the "Photo-Electric Effect." The Photo-Electric Effect details how photons (mass particles of light) carry energy. When photons strike a conductor such as a metal plate, the metal plate ejects and electron with energy in relation to how much charge the photon has on it. So

photons basically convert into electrical energy, the basis for Solar Power.

But if we examine the wave properties of photons in the electromagnetic spectrum, we can see that Planck and Einstein were both correct once again. Today, as scientists take measurements of the energy in photons in the electromagnetic spectrum, they find that photons in the lower spectrum (visible light) have energies of 1 electron Volt (1eV) and photons in the higher spectrum of light (Gamma) have energies of 1 Million electron Volts (1MeV).

If we examine the electromagnetic waves in the visible light spectrum, we can see that they are vibrating at a rate starting at around a quadrillion Hertz (1 quadrillion waves per second). In the Gamma Spectrum, the number of waves per second is so high that waves oscillate at a sextillion times per second. This establishes the fact that the more frequently electromagnetic waves oscillate per second (measured in Hertz), the more energy the photons resonating with that wave frequency carry.

Einstein saw energy in the form of heat and light. While nuclear power plants convert heat into electricity, they are very inefficient. Transforming the heat of a nuclear reaction into usable steam to turn electrical power generators results in a great loss of the initial energy. It is also radioactive.

Planck observed that heat energy failed to excite higher frequency light waves, such as ultraviolet rays, unless the temperature of the heat was made to be very high. The high frequency waves simply cost to much energy. This was because it took energy to create the heat. The energy needed to create such high heat energy waves would consume more energy than one could obtain out of a closed system. This demonstrates that high frequency light waves radiate and represent more energy than lower frequency light waves.

Sources of Electrical Energy

What if a machine could produce high-frequency waves of magnetic energy using a small amount of input energy and convert such high frequency energy into lower and usable frequency electricity, obviating the heat cycle common to nuclear power plants? Would we see a generation of electrical power devices that produce more energy than one needs to start such a system? According to Planck's theory, there should be much more energy in high frequency waves of energy than there is in lower frequency electrical energy. Would the cost of producing high frequency waves using magnetic devices instead of heat systems be sufficient to see an over all energy gain when the high frequency waves are converted back into lower waves?

A system like this would break the existing laws of "The conservation of energy" and the "Law of thermodynamics." These laws state that you cannot get more energy out of a system than you put into it.

The idea of breaking the laws of thermodynamics and conservation of energy are not new. In nuclear fusion devices, the hope is to see more energy coming out of a system than is being used to ignite the system. In fact, nuclear fission reactors are already doing this. They produce more energy than it takes to ignite the reaction. But, we do know that such systems are radioactive.

All of this discussion about energy is directly related to UFOs because they need vast amounts of energy to possibly travel at light speed and even more energy to break light speed. If they were using nuclear powered energy for space travel, they would have a better chance of doing near light speed. But to break light speed, they would have to be utilizing such high frequency magnetic waves, that they are able to transform their whole craft and crew into such a high frequency wave state. Once in that high frequency wave form, they could conquer the vast distances of space and not be affected by impacting with debris and planets while in such high speed transit: they would have to make their craft and crew into such a high frequency wave of energy that they would pass right through all matter just as neutrinos pass right through matter as though it were not even there.

When Max Planck discovered that Energy is equal to the frequency of oscillating magnetic waves, he demonstrated that higher frequency magnetic waves produced more energy than lower frequency magnetic waves. This is elementary in his principle discovery. How do we translate higher frequency waves into usable energy? Because we use electricity in a lower frequency wave-form, we would have to convert it back to the frequency we use energy at. How much energy does it take to produce such high frequency waves? Once we converted such high frequency waves back to a lower form of energy, would we see an energy gain or loss? Or, could we use energy on a higher frequency to operate all of our mechanical devices with a quantum leap in energy efficiency?

Planck's Constant and the Energy of a Photon

In 1900, Max Planck was working on the problem of how the radiation an object emits is related to its energy or temperature. He came up with a formula (E = hf) that agreed very closely with experimental data, but the formula only made sense if he assumed that the energy of a vibrating molecule was quantized—that is, it could only take on certain values. The energy would have to be proportional to the frequency of vibration, and it seemed to come in little "chunks" of the frequency multiplied by a certain constant. This constant came to be known as "Planck's constant," or h, and it has the value

$$h = 6.626 \times 10^{-34} \, J \cdot s$$

I would later apply Planck's basic formula and alter it for a new theory to explain Gravity (electromagnetism) Beyond Light Speed.

Remember, most physicists and astrophysicists cannot explain the great mystery of gravity. It is the greatest mystery in science today. Scientists have ideas that gravity may be able to bend light and be stronger than light, but there is no existing theory that works to explain it.

II – Gravity (Electromagnetism) Beyond Light Speed Theory
By: David Sereda, January 10, 2000

In the late afternoon of January 10th, 2000, I had a revelation on a new theory that would explain the gradient frequencies of gravity in a mathematical formula and model that resembles our own galaxy.

The model and theory would show that, using light as a constant speed, gradient levels of Electromagnetism/Gravity would appear and eventually pass beyond light speed, and then so far beyond light speed that the entire 100,000 light year diameter of our own Milky Way galaxy could be conquered in zero time by the highest frequency of gravity in the galaxy. Beyond the galaxy, gravity waves could radiate so high in frequency that they could conquer the entire universe in zero time.

The point in this theory would be to teach us how to produce and recognize these different frequencies of gravity for our own use in quantum physics and quantum space travel technologies. Because what we were about to witness in the NASA UFOs was evidence of craft traveling on faster than light gravity waves, we would need to understand a theory that could explain that. The UFOs would also reveal to us the signature of their propulsion system and it would fit perfectly into the physical model of my "Gravity Beyond Light Speed Theory" perhaps giving evidence to support the theory. It would also explain "electron shifts," "red shifting" AND OTHER Quantum ideas perfectly.

Perpetual Motion?

The idea of a perpetual motion machine is against the law in the United States Patent Office. If a person files for a patent claiming perpetual motion, they will immediately be declined. This is because perpetual motion machines break the laws of thermodynamics and conservation of energy. To break those laws is to break the law of the United States Patent Office.

Our own galaxy is breaking those laws because it is a perfect example of a giant machine that is in a state of perpetual motion. Our galaxy is 100,000 light years in diameter: it takes light 100,000 years to cross the galaxy. The mass in our galaxy is turning like a giant wheel at a rate of one revolution approximately every 250,000,000 years. It is like a giant clock. If we consider the entire mass of the galaxy, and consider how much energy it would take to turn that mass in a constant state of perpetual motion, where would all the energy come from?

If God created the perpetual motion of the galaxy, God would be denied a U.S. patent for breaking the laws of "Conservation of Energy" and "The Law of Thermodynamics." There must be something about the galaxy that can teach us how to build a perpetual motion machine, but even more so, how to show the theory of "Gravity Beyond Light Speed," I thought.

This is because modern astronomy and science knows that a black hole in the center of a galaxy is absorbing all light and all mass. Scientists don't really know what a black hole is and where it gets all of its energy from, but they do know that it is doing what it does: absorbing all light and mass.

To start my new theory, I will use a model of what I call (my invention) a "Galaxy Clock" (see model on next page) to demonstrate the gradient frequencies of gravity. In this new theory, gravity frequencies are electromagnetic waves, which include "visible light" as just one frequency bandwidth of electromagnetic waves. In this Galaxy Clock, I will use light speed as what I call a relative constant speed and I will use gravity as another relative measure that is gradient and therefore not constant. Each gradient measure of gravity is constant in its own particular frequency.

Because light speed is the only constant in modern physics, the constant distance light travels per second (186,282 miles per second) will be used as a measurement on 10 wheels radiating out from the relative center of the Galaxy Clock. On each wheel, the same distance that light travels per second will be used starting from the "0" position and moving counter clockwise from the outer most wheel towards the inner most wheel.

The straight line connecting the "0" position of the outer most wheel to the center of the inner most wheel represents Gravity Force, Space and Time. The distance from the "0" position to the "1" position is the constant distance used on the Galaxy Clock for the distance light travels per second. The distance is constant because it represents the only constant in known physics: light. Each count on the Galaxy Clock uses the same relative distance regardless of the size of the wheel it is moving over.

The phase-1 diagram of the Galaxy Clock goes from 0 – 12 counts. We can see that the Gravity Force, Space and Time line becomes curved and actually grows in length (if we uncoiled it) by the time we get to the 12-count position. The growth and curvature of this line represents the increase in Gravity Force, Space and Decrease of the Time it takes for Gravity to conquer space distances.

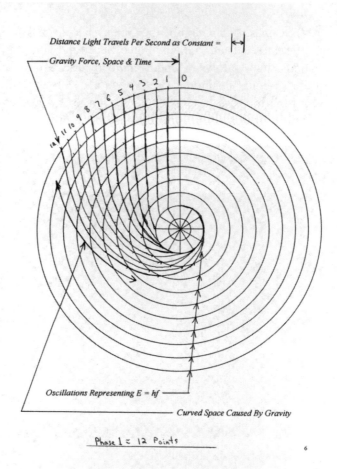

Distance Light Travels Per Second as Constant =

Gravity Force, Space & Time →

0 1 2 3 4 5 6 7 8 9 10 11 12

Oscillations Representing E = hf

Curved Space Caused By Gravity

Phase 1 = 12 Points

Phase 1 of galaxy Clock

This Galaxy Clock was created by using the constant speed of light distance like a second hand on a regular clock. Each distance the second hand travels on this clock is equal to the distance light travels per second (186,282 miles). Each second of light speed distance is the same on each of the ten wheels on the clock.

I then marked each second of light speed distance for the 12-counts used on this Galaxy Clock on each of the 10 wheels. Next, I connected the Gravity, Space and Time line through each of the relative seconds on each wheel. We can now see what happened.

In regards to faster oscillations representing higher frequency energy (Max Planck's E = hf), the outer wheel has made less than a 1/4th oscillation while the inner wheel has made its first complete oscillation in the 12-count position.

Using Planck's formula, I supposition his "h" as Planck's Constant for one Hertzian wave, thus modifying his theory slightly. While I modify Planck's theory, I make it my own theory based on Planck's original equation. Using my new understanding of Planck's equation (E = hf), the inner wheel should have produced more energy than the outer wheel and it did. The inner wheel is oscillating faster than the outer wheel, and therefore the inner wheel is oscillating at a higher frequency of energy than the outer wheel and should therefore be radiating a wave of greater energy than the outer wheel. This can easily be explained if we were to use a Tesla coil as an electromagnet.

The more windings of copper wire we wrap around a cylinder, the stronger the magnetic force becomes when we create an electromagnet. Electromagnets are essentially Tesla Coils. The more windings, the more energy comes through a Tesla Coil. This experiment demonstrates, in part, what is happening in the Galaxy Clock. However, it is only a small part.

If we see the Galaxy Clock as a coil for a moment, we can see that for the same distance electricity travels through a wire per second, the smaller winding in the center of the Galaxy Clock will produce more energy as an electromagnet than the outer wheel because the inner wheel actually completes an oscillation (and oscillates faster per second) while the outer wheel has not even completed a single oscillation. One oscillation is represented by one orbit around the center of the Galaxy Clock; thus one complete circuit. The more oscillations a wave makes per second, the more energy the wave produces.

This same observation can be made in the electromagnetic spectrum in regards to understanding light and light waves. Einstein won the Nobel Prize in Physics in 1921 for explaining "The Photo Electric Effect." What he demonstrated was that when photons strike a metal plate or a conductor, the metal plate ejects an electron. The electron has a charge of electricity on it. The more energy the photon carried, the more energy would be present in the electron. So photons basically convert into electrical energy, the basis for Solar Power.

But if we examine the electromagnetic wave properties of photons in the electromagnetic spectrum, we can see that Planck and Einstein were both correct once again. Today, as scientists take measurements of the energy in photons in the electromagnetic spectrum, they find that photons in the lower spectrum (visible light) have energies of 1 electron Volt (1eV) and photons in the higher spectrum of light (Gamma) have energies of 1 Million electron Volts (1MeV).

The accuracy of these current wave to energy conversions would later be challenged by new data from NASA taking measurements of the same wave in space producing even higher charges of energy from the photons. The idea of taking measurements above the atmosphere comes from the hypothesis that the Earth's atmosphere is reflecting most of the higher frequency light waves, thus preventing them from penetrating the atmosphere and entering the Earth. For now we would have to use the data provided by science.

If we examine the electromagnetic waves in the visible light spectrum, we can see that they are vibrating at a rate starting at around a quadrillion Hertz (1 quadrillion waves per second). In the Gamma Spectrum, the number of waves per second is so high that waves oscillate at a sextillion times per second. This establishes the fact that the more frequently electromagnetic waves oscillate per second (measured in Hertz), the more energy the photons resonating with that wave frequency carry.

When we look at the electromagnetic spectrum, we can see that Light is both waves, that have frequency (how frequently a wave oscillates per second measured in Hertzian waves), and mass particles called photons. Science has discovered that Gamma Photons carry a lot more energy than Visible light photons. When we look at the waves in the gamma spectrum, we can see that they oscillate faster per second than visible light photons. Therefore, they should have more energy due to the greater oscillations per second in their waves.

My new theory takes Max Planck's E = hf (Energy is equal to the Frequency of the Oscillation of a wave) with a new definition that is proven by the nature of Light and the Electromagnetic Spectrum. The Galaxy Clock demonstrates this all more precisely.

This Galaxy Clock is not to be reduced to an electrical coil. I am only using a coil as an example to prove the point that Max Planck made in the early 1900s: that greater oscillations of energy create higher frequency and more energy than lower or slower oscillations of energy. Our own Galaxy is starting to show us where it gets all of its energy from and where that energy originates from: the center or zero-point.

If we look at the point where the outer wheel 12-count Gravity Force, Space and Time line strikes the inner wheel (in counter clockwise) it almost touches (8.5) and touches at the 8-count position and then has to move all the way to the 12-count position from the outer wheel to the inner most wheel all in the same second. The curvature of the Gravity line, which is the frequency of gravity, represents this increase in gravity/magnetic energy. The spread equals 4.5 counts on the Galaxy Clock. This represents a Gravity Force (electromagnetic wave) moving 4.5 times the speed of light in the same relative second. This happened without any input of extra energy into the Galaxy Clock.

This shows that each connecting count on the outer wheel with the innermost wheel represents a frequency of gravity. These frequencies are infinite in their precise measurements. The frequencies increase with each movement towards the innermost wheel. I am only using 10 wheels to demonstrate the principle. The number of wheels can be infinite to express more precise frequencies of Gravity Force, Space and Time.

We can also now witness how similar the Gravity Clock appears to a photograph of one of the spiral arms of a galaxy. This model demonstrates the physics of light and gravity in a real galaxy. It works mathematically to produce an actual galaxy spiral arm because this is how a galaxy is working in actual fact according to this theory.

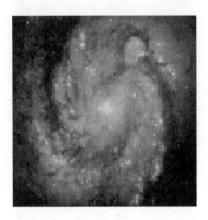

Core of Galaxy M-100

Because the Galaxy Clock experiment reveals the workings of a Galaxy and details what is happening as electromagnetic waves move into smaller and smaller orbits (waves increase in frequency with light as a constant speed), we can now start to understand a Black Hole in the core of every Galaxy.

This theory reveals that a black hole at the relative core of a galaxy is a relative mass and wave of gravity energy spinning faster than light speed, just as the 12-count position on the Gravity Clock revealed that the Gravity Force in the center of the wheel is moving 4.5 times the speed of light. Because the human eye and camera sees events in relative light speed time, when a force of gravity frequency goes beyond relative light speed, relative light cannot reflect off of it nor radiate from it, thus it appears to be black: void of relative light speed time observations of light.

But my new theory would also challenge current beliefs about Black Holes. This theory says that a Black Hole is the place where oscillations per second in electromagnetic waves are so much higher than even Gamma Waves, that the energy produced would move towards infinity. Because the energy required for mass to move at the speed of light is a fixed number, and the electromagnetic waves oscillate at higher and higher frequencies per second as they move into smaller and smaller orbits (towards infinity), and as they oscillate with greater frequency they produce more electromagnetic energy (energy increasing towards infinity), they will eventually produce more energy than is required for photons or any high frequency mass to attain the speed of light. Once the energy levels in the electromagnetic field conquer the point that is required to break the speed of light, mass, now affected by these ultra-high frequency electromagnetic waves, can break the speed of light. The Galaxy Clock experiment proves this.

Due to my new modification of Planck's theory (E = hf), It would reveal that Black Holes are not heavy at all. In fact, as any mass came in contact with higher frequency waves, the mass of an object would become so high in frequency; thus making it lighter and lighter until that mass became as light as a photon (basically with nearly zero mass) and that mass would be able to accelerate with absolute ease towards the speed of light and beyond.

Nikola Tesla and Schumann detected that the Earth is vibrating between 7 and 8 Hertz, a very low frequency wave state compared to Photons. Tesla detected that most mass objects on the Earth vibrated with a frequency similar to that of the Earth. Although all mass objects have a precise and unique frequency, everything known to us that we can touch as a solid mass object is vibrating within the lower frequency wave state of the Earth.

This reveals to us that the difference between solid mass and energy is detailed in the frequency of its wave state. Everything known to science is vibrating with particular frequencies. But what the Galaxy Clock experiment reveals is that mass can change frequency, thus its properties and its ability to attain the speed of light is proportional to its frequency.

Einstein did not take this into consideration: that as mass comes into contact with higher frequency electromagnetic waves, the mass of that object reduces making it lighter rather than increasing proportional to E = mc2. This is because Einstein saw mass remaining at the same frequency trying to accelerate towards the speed of light. In a low frequency state, mass cannot attain the speed of light. He was right.

Canadian Scientist John Hutchison is the inventor of the "Hutchison Effect." I met with him in the year 2000 to discuss his findings and show him the Galaxy Clock experiment. He basically was the first scientist to demonstrate that by pulsing a low frequency mass object with higher frequency electromagnetic waves, he could change the frequency of the object and cause its mass to reduce so greatly that it would levitate.

In one recent to the year 2000 experiment, he pulsed a 70-lb canon ball with high frequency waves from a Van De Graff generator, a Tesla Coil and high Frequency Tesla radio waves going all the way up into the Gigahertz (billion Hertz) range. When the canon ball's low frequency wave state (7-8 Hertz) changed into a higher frequency wave state, it levitated, thus proving the theory. It was also the greatest break-through on levitation of our time.

When Hutchison studied the Galaxy Clock experiment, he agreed with its findings, and he understood how it applied to his experiments on levitation.

Hutchison was also able to tap into higher frequency waves of energy and actually extract some of that energy and produce permanent power cell batteries.

If mass changes frequency as it comes in contact with higher frequency waves (see Hutchison Effect) from a lower 7-8 Hertz wave state (most matter on Earth) into a higher frequency wave state such as photons vibrate at (1,000 Hertz Radio Photons – 1 sextillion Hertz Gamma Photons), then mass is reducing and can thus break Einstein's law and attain the speed of light and even break the speed of light. The Galaxy Clock experiment is demonstrating this.

Without light even traveling 1/4th revolution on the outer most wheel of the Galaxy Clock, the innermost wheel made a full revolution and the Gravity Force, Space and Time line increased to 4.5 times the speed of light. This increase in energy is the energy the galaxy uses to perpetually keep itself moving. If the galaxy did not produce more energy than it takes to run the galaxy, the galaxy would quickly reach entropy and die. It does not die, therefore this theory must be correct in showing where the galaxy is getting its perpetual energy. But there is so much more to this theory. What will happen if we go another 12-counts on the Gravity Clock?

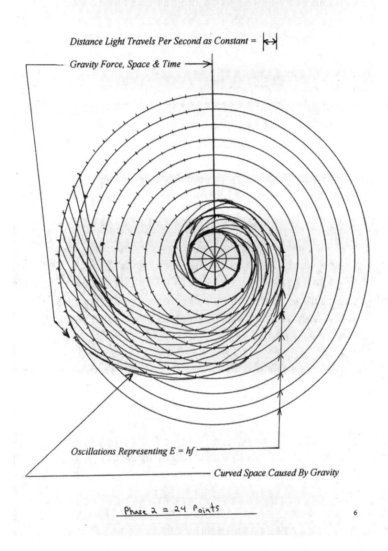

Distance Light Travels Per Second as Constant = |←→|

Gravity Force, Space & Time ——→

Oscillations Representing E = hf

Curved Space Caused By Gravity

Phase 2 = 24 Points

6

Phase 2 of Galaxy Clock

On Phase 2 of the Gravity Clock, using the constant speed of light-distance per second, we have started on this clock with the 12-count position and move towards the 24-count position.

The straight line of "0" is so curved at the 12-count position that it has grown in length. This length is also relative to Space in the same count of one second of light speed time. The growth in this line also possibly suggests that Gravity Force is actually creating space. This reveals that gravity, the dark and mysterious luminosity of the universe is actually creating distance and space, yet conquering it at the same time.

As previously observed in Phase 1 of the Galaxy Clock, at the 12-count position, the curve of the gravity line is so steep, it moves over 4.5 times the speed of light (4.5 times the speed of light per second) in the inner most wheel of the galaxy clock.

The speed of light is broken in principle here only. It is actually broken when low frequency mass (such as a spacecraft) comes into contact with higher frequency waves and the higher energy in the waves. When the mass of a spacecraft is reduced to that equal to photons and even lighter, and the energy in the waves is high enough, the spacecraft can attain and break the speed of light. The Galaxy Clock Experiment is showing us how to do this. In order for a spacecraft to attain light speed (186,282 miles per second), it has to change the frequency of its mass from a low wave state of 7-8 Hertz to a higher frequency wave state equal to that of photons (1,000 – 1 sextillion Hertz).

At the 24-count position on the Galaxy Clock, the inner wheel has made 2 oscillations. The Gravity Force, Space and Time line touched the inner wheel at the 6-count position and moved to the 12-count position, it then continued all the way around for another full oscillation to reach the 24-count position in one second (curve). If we add 6 and 12 together, we get 18. This means that gravity has exponentially jumped from 4.5 times the speed of light in the 12-count position to 18.5+ times the speed of light in the 24-count position. This shows an exponential increase in Gravity Force energy. Note that the 0.5 counts are due to the fact that the steeper the Gravity Force line approaches the inner wheel, while it doesn't touch it in the 0.5 position, it is so close that I added 0.5 counts to it.

Using my modification of Max Planck's $E = hf$, we can see that the center wheel has oscillated 2 times while the outer most wheel has oscillated $1/3^{rd}$ of an oscillation. While the inner wheel is oscillating 2 times at the 24-count position, the curvature of the Gravity Force line has moved 18.5 times the speed of light and the length of the Gravity Force, Space and Time line is growing exponentially. Gravity is conquering greater and greater distances in the galaxy with exponential increases in the same second of light speed time and distance around the Galaxy Clock. Gravity is growing, space distances are being conquered by it and time is remaining the same for light speed. As we can see what is happening here and where this is going, gravity has gradient frequencies that start at zero and move towards infinity with exponential increases.

Gravity Energy has frequencies, which can be measured in grades of 0-24 on this Galaxy Clock. Gravity conquers light speed at about the 5-count position on the Galaxy Clock by going 1.25 times light speed.
At the 7-count position on the Galaxy Clock, gravity goes 2.5 times the speed of light. At the 12-count position, Gravity goes 4.5 times light speed.

It is important to note that all of the gradient frequencies of gravity already exist in the universe by this theory. They have already been created by our galaxy. If we could tune the frequency of a space craft to these same higher frequencies of gravity (magnetic waves), perhaps we could make quantum leaps in space travel through space in less and less amounts of time until we reach a frequency of gravity that can conquer the distance of our own galaxy in zero time. After that, we may begin to visit other galaxies in very little time.

A new phenomenon is now witnessed on the Galaxy Clock that did not exist in the Phase 1 model. At the 24-count position, while the outer-most wheel has made nearly $1/3^{rd}$ of an oscillation, the 2nd wheel out from the inner-most wheel has mad 1 ¼ oscillations and the 3rd wheel out from the inner-most wheel has made 1 oscillation. This is representing an out-going wave caused by the exponential increase in oscillations at the relative inner-most wheel. This shows an inward-moving gradient spiral frequency of gravity in tandem with an outward expanding and oscillating wave. The Alpha and the Omega, the Micro universe working in tandem with the Macro universe.

Physicists Break The Speed of Light

In 1998, press reports revealed that Dr. Raymond Chiao, a Professor of Physics at Berkeley, California caused photons (particles of light) to travel faster than the speed of the light. Dr. Chiao made the discovery by causing photons to "tunnel" through barriers such as glass sheets and the "tunneling" photon would arrive at the other side faster than a photon traveling in tandem with no barrier; and thus no tunneling effect. Why was this happening?

Chiao turned his attention towards the quantum phenomenon of "tunneling" occurring when a particle runs into a wall or barrier that it can't go through or around. Instead it simply seems to disappear and instantly reappears on the other side. Chiao applied this to photons, the fastest particles thus so far measured (light speed).

When Dr. Raymond Chiao carried out experiments, each photon in the race that tunneled through a barrier arrived 1.5 femtoseconds sooner than its race mate suggesting it had tunneled through the barrier at 1.7 times the speed of light. Raymond Chiao is as surprised as everyone. While physicists all over the world stand in disbelief, it is really happening.

Chiao couldn't even explain why it was happening, but utilizing the technology to measure the speed of atomic particles (atomic clocks), photons that "tunneled through barriers arrived as much as 1.7 times the speed of light." This would change everything we knew about Einstein "relativity" if Chiao was right. But Chiao would also have to be able to explain what and why this was happening.

When I applied the model of my Galaxy Clock, I could see the answer staring me right in the face. It was so obvious I almost need not say. The Galaxy Clock shows a model of photons tunneling in smaller and smaller orbits around a nucleus. The smaller the orbit, the more revolutions (oscillations) a photon makes per second. The oscillations per second increase as the tunnel gets smaller and smaller.

This is demonstrated if we take a piece of copper wire that represents the distance light travels per second, and we make a big circle with it, it only makes one circle or oscillation per second. But if we take the same piece of wire and make a smaller series of circles, we have more oscillations or revolutions per second.

In electromagnetism, the more revolutions an electric current makes around a nucleus, the stronger the magnetic field created gets. This is demonstrated perfectly when we try to make an electromagnet. The more windings of cooper wire around a pole we make, the stronger the magnetic field gets.

What I have just demonstrated is so obvious to anyone with scientific intelligence. Dr. Raymond Chiao's speeding photons are "tunneling" through barriers and arriving at the other side faster than light. Do you know the answer?

Raymond Chiao's "tunneling photons" are spiraling, just as demonstrated in the Galaxy Clock as they move through the barrier placed for them to travel through. The micro "tunneling" of the photons is producing a powerful ultra-high frequency electromagnetic field in the vortex, which then pulls the photons through by its gravity or electromagnetic force. Because the "tunnels" are so micro-atomic in size, the revolutions (oscillations) per second for the speed of light photons is phenomenally high. This extremely high rate of oscillation creates frequencies of gravity (electromagnetism) that are so powerful (see Galaxy Clock experiment), they cause the photons to travel faster than the speed of light. To the exact degree, the frequency of gravity, as demonstrated in the Galaxy Clock, is relative to how much faster or slower a photon can move through the electromagnetic spectrum.

On July 20, 2000, The Toronto Star in Canada reported that "Scientists Break Speed-Of-Light Barrier." The article stated that, "Scientists have apparently broken the universe's speed limit. For generations, physicists believed there is nothing faster than light moving through a vacuum." The news would change the face of science and Einstein's limitations would be broken. It was the death of the old world and the birth of a new age of physics.

But in an experiment in Princeton, N.J., physicists sent a pulse of laser light through cesium vapor so quickly it left the chamber before it had even finished entering.

The article also stated that, "The pulse traveled 310 times the distance it would have covered if the chamber had contained a vacuum. Researchers said it is the most convincing demonstration yet that the speed of light - supposedly an ironclad rule of nature - can be pushed beyond known boundaries, at least under certain laboratory circumstances."

"This effect cannot be used to send information back in time," said Lijun Wang, a researcher with the private NEC Institute. "However, our experiment does show that the generally-held misconception that 'nothing can travel faster than the speed of light' is wrong." The results were published in Thursday's issue of the journal Nature. Not everyone is convinced the NEC scientists did what they claim.

Aephraim Steinberg, a physicist at the University of Toronto, said the light particles coming out of the cesium chamber may not have been the same ones that entered, so he questions whether the speed of light was broken.

Still, the work is important, he said: "The interesting thing is how did they manage to produce light that looks exactly like something that didn't get there yet?"

Dr. Raymond Chiao, who already succeeded in breaking light speed with "tunneling" photons said "This is a breakthrough in the sense that people have thought that was impossible.'" He was not involved in the work.

The implications to this are so staggering, I cannot explain my deepest thoughts. But now how could all of this be applied to making space craft travel beyond the speed of light so that humankind could reach its nearest star systems in a reasonable amount of time?

III- The NASA UFOs Reveal Amazing Evidence

I once asked Dr. Glenn Seaborg, while he was Chairman of the Advanced Physics Corporation (Noble Laureate who invented plutonium and Chaired the Atomic Energy Commission under Presidents Kennedy, Johnson and Nixon) about anti-gravity devices being developed by alternative energy developers. The correct term for such energy systems is "Zero-Point Energy." He answered me and said, "If anyone could build a gravity generator, they would have an energy source beyond nuclear fusion and we wouldn't be doing this: trying to help Dr. Maglich's fusion technology become a reality. Such a device would be able to tap into an endless supply of electricity and I don't believe anyone is doing anything like that yet."

Dr. Glenn Seaborg was unaware of a vast movement of alternative electrical engineers who were tapping into a new source of "Zero-Point" energy using magnetic devices. The Zero-Point is a quantum vacuum, void of all magnetism where the quantum energy of the alleged "ether" flows through continuously. It was and still "is" an energy source that cannot be explained by conventional physics, just like "electron-shifts" and "red-shifts" cannot be explained.

In 1905, Einstein rejected the idea that the void of space was filled with energy waves or charged particles. Ten years after, Einstein's own developments of the general theory of relativity forced him to reverse his stance. Einstein now believed that the void of space may indeed be filled with unseen energy. This was the basis for Zero-Point Energy.

Dr. Hal Puthoff at the Institute for Advanced Studies at Austin Texas submitted a paper to NASA's new "Breakthrough Propulsion Physics Workshop," at NASA's Lewis Research Center in Cleveland, Ohio, August 12-14, 1997. The paper was entitled, "Can the Vacuum be Engineered for Spaceflight Applications?" In this paper, Dr. Puthoof explains that, "Quantum theory predicts, and experiments verify, that empty space (the vacuum) contains an enormous residual background energy known as zero-point energy (ZPE). ZPE topics of interest for spaceflight applications range from fundamental issues (where does inertia come from, can it be controlled?), through laboratory attempts to extract useful energy from vacuum fluctuations (can ZPE be "mined" for practical use?), to scientifically-grounded extrapolations concerning "engineering the vacuum" (is "warp-drive" space propulsion a scientific possibility?). Recent advances in research into the physics of the underlying ZPE indicate the possibility of potential application in all these areas of interest.

On January 13, 2000, I was flown to somewhere in the United States to meet with one of the world's leading Zero-Point energy developers. He was interested in seeing the NASA UFOs. I spent the next month sharing the NASA video footage with him and learning about the Zero-Point energy and how it was created.

A Zero-Point energy is best described as the center point in the Galaxy Clock where magnetic fields of energy oscillate at such a high frequency, that the inertial time response of magnetism cannot catch up with the fast pace of the oscillating magnetic field and thus produces a magnetic vacuum where there is no more inertia.

With no more inertia (resistance caused by mass), energy flows through this vacuum at speeds (frequencies) greater than light speed. In fact, this is where Einstein was correct about mass not being able to move at light speeds. Mass, as it is, cannot do this. This is because mass acts as resistance to the flow of energy. As mass increases, it takes an infinite amount of energy for the increasing mass to move at light speed. But if this mass started to vibrate at a higher and higher frequency, it would no longer act as resistance (inertia) to relative energy.

Little known, in 1972, three physicists won the Nobel Prize in physics for a discovery that proved the zero-point energy equation. John Bardeen, Leon Cooper and J. Robert Shrieffer won the prize "for their jointly developed theory of superconductivity, usually called BCS-theory."

The phenomenon of superconductivity was discovered by Dutch physicist Kamerling Onnes already in 1911. Already his first measurements indicated that one had found a fundamentally new state of matter. The term superconductivity refers to the complete disappearance of the electrical resistance. To eliminate resistance, is the same as eliminating inertia: the force that prevents energy from

flowing more efficiently and at greater speeds. Many remarkable properties were discovered in the following decades.

The main problem, the question about the underlying mechanism for superconductivity, remained a mystery up to the late 1950s. The difference in energy between the superconducting and the normal state in metals is extremely small in comparison with all typical energies in a metal and therefore many different mechanisms might be possible. A significant step forward was taken around 1950 when it was found theoretically and experimentally that the mechanism for superconductivity had to do with coupling of electrons to the vibrations of their crystal lattice. Starting from this mechanism, Bardeen, Cooper and Shrieffer developed a theory of superconductivity in 1957, which gave a complete theoretical explanation of the phenomenon.

Their new theory demonstrated that the interaction between the electrons and the lattice leads to the formation of bound pairs of electrons, which are often called "Copper Pairs." The different pairs are strongly coupled to each other which leads to a complex collective pattern (time forward electron pairs with a time reversed electron) in which a considerable fraction of the total number of conduction electrons are coupled together to form the superconducting state.

The anonymous zero-point energy scientist I was studying with describes the same phenomenon happening in the zero point energy flux: that a proprietary method of spinning magnets or electromagnets causes the forces of Inertia (resistance) to become suspended. With the suspension of relative inertia, the natural and abundant levels of higher frequency magnetic energy, flow through the zero point. In essence, by suspending inertia, a bridge is formed for these higher and omnipresent energies to flow in through. This solved Max Planck's greatest problem: how to produce higher frequency waves and then transfer the higher frequency gain of energy back down into a frequency of electricity where it could be used in modern mechanical devices with a gain in energy.

The work of these 1972 Nobel Prize winners was validated in Zero-Point energy machines yet the United States Patent office refuses to give patents for these devices out of fear they there is some kind of trickery going on. No one can explain where the extra energy is coming from in these zero-point energy machines, not but least, the inventors themselves.

Bardeen, Cooper and Schreiffer didn't have a zero-point energy machine to explain and validate their theories either. But they did set the stage in physics for a new theory in energy.

Based on the proprietary information I learned from my anonymous Zero-Point energy scientist, we both discovered a new equation for energy. His theory was that energy is not created out of "nothing" in a zero-point energy machine. His theory was that higher frequencies of energy are omnipresent all throughout time and space, just as my new "Gravity Beyond Light Speed Theory – Jan 10, 2000) stated. Those higher frequency energies just need a bridge to flow through. By reducing the force of inertia with a zero-point energy flux of magnetic patterns, that abundant energy flows in through the space of the zero-point field.

Our new equation was that Energy (E) increases as Inertia (I) decreases in frequency (h). "E = Ih" would be the explanation for Zero-Point Energy. The greater the ratio between high and low frequencies, the lower is the resistance created by inertia, and the more energy flows in from higher gravity frequencies. This would supply the missing "cause" to produce Max Planck's higher frequency energy waves without creating a bonfire. As inertia decreased, the higher frequency energy waves would spontaneously arise out of the ether. But what was the ether thought of?

There has been a huge debate in physics: is space an empty void of all subatomic particles with no energy or mass? The question remained: Is there an ether" filled with energy? New and astounding evidence to prove that space is not a dead void, but filled with tremendous energy, surfaced at NASA by Dr. Louis A. Frank's research. I read about it in the package of information he sent me.

When photographs of the Earth taken by the special ultraviolet camera on board the NASA Polaris satellite in 1997 were digitally processed, they revealed a tremendous amount of "effects of penetrating electrons from the radiation zone into the sensor of the Earth Camera." The images were taken from the satellite at an altitude of 17,937 kilometers.

Left - Perhaps Millions of 2.7-14 MeV Electrons

Dr. Louis A. Frank's data revealed these amazing photos of high-energy electrons penetrating into the camera's sensor used on the satellite. The left image is described as "A worst-case example of the effects of penetrating electrons from the radiation zone into the sensor of the Earth Camera on the Polaris satellite. The image on the right was taken "after a simple algorithm is used to reduce the amplitudes of the pixel response increases due to the penetrating particles."

It was recorded by scientists that these electrons were charged with an average of 2.7 MeV (Million Electron Volts). Some were measured as high as 14 MeV. The electron intensities were simultaneously measured with the HIST on board this same spacecraft (courtesy of J.B. Blake and R.S. Selesnick).

There were thousands of these electrons. Space is filled with them. Space is not a dead vacuum as the new evidence revealed. 2.7 MeV electrons are about as charged as the energy present in the cold fusion of Deuterium. D+D fusion produces 3.67 MeV per fusion, 33 percent of which is energy charged neutrons. That leaves about 2.45 MeV of usable energy per fusion.

If space in the Far Ultraviolet wavelengths is proven now to be filled with 2.7 MeV and greater energy electrons, the current data of

1 thousand electron Volt energies in the Ultraviolet wavelengths would be challenged and proven wrong.

Is there a way that a technology could utilize and gather such energies for space travel? Could the Zero-Point energy (quantum vacuum) be utilized in space to gather these charges particles? Is this where the amazing zero-point energy is coming from: empty space but space filled with electrons of very high energy? Would science be able to tap into this inexhaustible supply of electron energies by applying the works of Max Planck, Tesla and the Zero-Point energy developers?

The photos of penetrating high-energy electrons taken by NASA's Polaris satellite in 1997 now proved that the quantum theory of a zero-point vacuum filled with energy was correct. Einstein's fears that space was empty and void of energy and charged particles back in 1905 was now confirmed to be incorrect, and that his later assessment in 1915 was correct. The void of space is seething with charged particles. But to access these higher energies, we would have to produce higher frequency electromagnetic waves as the Galaxy Clock experiment shows.

Dr. Hal Puthoff wrote in his paper to NASA's "Breakthrough Propulsion Physics Workshop" in 1997, that "It was the advent of modern quantum theory, however, that established the quantum vacuum, so-called empty space, as a very active place, with particles arising and disappearing, a virtual plasma, and fields continuously fluctuating about their zero-point energy (ZPE), reflecting the fact that such activity remains even at absolute zero."

The real challenge now lied in the engineering of tapping into the zero-point field of energy. Just as my modification of Max Planck had discovered in $E = hf$ (Energy is Equal to the frequency of an oscillating wave), so the Zero-Point reveals that the center of the Galaxy Clock is oscillating at a tremendously high frequency, reducing inertia ($E = Ih$) and causing energy to flow in through the zero-point vacuum. When that center Zero-Point energy field vibrated at a sufficiently high frequency, the out-going wave (refer to Galaxy Clock Phase 2 model) would affect everything it contacted with the same high frequency Zero-Point energy.

This Zero-Point energy scientist I was studying with bought a 32-inch TV and a super VHS video player to see the UFOs more clearly. We were interested one day in seeing the pulsing waves of energy radiating from the UFOs on the STS-75 tether incident in slow motion and then frame-by-frame. When we slowed them down to frame by frame, we were both astounded to see the first evidence in history of actually being able to see that the UFOs were communicating to us the example of how they conquered the vast distances of space and time. It was the Galaxy Clock and the Zero-Point energy field right in front of our faces. We were both astounded to say the least.

If a gravity source beyond light speed could be developed, it could bend light waves in grades or curves that can be measured. Although we cannot see a gravity wave, we can see light itself and view phenomena in relative light speed time. If a gravity wave that was vibrating faster than light energy could bend light into the curved shape of the wave itself, light would reflect off of, or be created by the gravity wave. Then, for the first time, we could see a gravity wave that is faster than light.

I present evidence of this in 3 still-photos of a UFO that was videotaped on the NASA STS-75 mission on February 25, 1996. The UFO was pulsing with a 3-phase, high-speed, continuously repeating gravity wave that fits perfectly into the model of the Galaxy Clock in my year 2000 "Gravity Beyond Light Speed Theory." The photos were taken off of the 32-inch TV monitor when the video was on "pause" and then frame-by-frame I saw the same three-phase pulse repeat itself over and over.

First Photo of 3-Phase Pulse

The first photo in the 3-phase gravity-light-pulse-wave emanating off of the UFO shows a spiral gravity wave just like the ones in the Galaxy Clock on my "Gravity Beyond Light Speed Theory."

It is very important to note than in the NASA video, these discs are pulsing with waves of light, which when slowed down to fractions of a second reveal wave patterns. My theory is that these UFOs are pulsing with gravity waves that are stronger than light, and can therefore bend light into the shape of the gravity wave. This allows us to observe the very first gravity beyond light speed "gravity wave." When the space shuttle cameras zoomed back, we could witness that the UFOs (now balls of light) had a light flashing to them; hence the pulses.

If we consider that the degree of the curvature of a gravity wave relative to the Galaxy Clock diagram represents a particular frequency of gravity, we can measure the strength of the gravity wave emanating from the UFO. The curvature of this gravity wave measured on the Galaxy Clock suggests a 21-count position. This position equals approximately 13.5 times the speed of light gravity wave. This does not suggest that the gravity wave is moving 13.5 times the speed of light, rather it is capable of moving the UFO at that speed. In the center of the gravity wave on the UFO, we can assume that there is a magnetic, perhaps Zero-Point energy system at work.

This theory reveals the black dot in the center of the UFO to be the same as the inner most wheel on the model of the "Galaxy Clock." This black dot is hypothesized by this theory to be a magnetic wave oscillating faster than light speed, and therefore, very much like a mini black hole. Because the gravity wave spins faster than relative light speed, we cannot see relative light speed reflecting off of it; thus it appears to be black.

Are the UFOs communicating something to us, which points in the direction of telling us where we need to develop our physics? Are they inadvertently showing us the future of our own capabilities for energy and space travel? Let us continue examining the remaining two pulses emanating from the UFO.

Second Photo of 3-Phase Pulse

The second photo of the UFO shows the second wave of its repeating 3-phase pulse. It shows an outward-radiating wave shaped like a ring moving towards the periphery of the UFO. This is also demonstrated on the Galaxy Clock.

At the 24-count position on the outer wheel of the Gravity Clock, the next phenomena was observed. The inner wheel had made 2 oscillations, while the second wheel made 1.4 oscillations and the third wheel made 1 oscillation creating an outward-radiating gravity wave. This is exactly what was happening with the UFOs pulsing wave sequence.

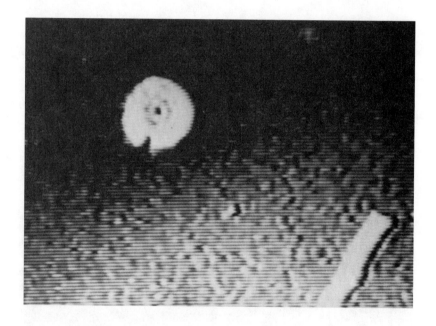

Third Photo of 3-Phase Pulse

The third photo of the 3-phase pulse emanating from the UFO shows that once the wave reached the periphery of the UFO (circle), it bounces back towards the center and forms an inward moving ring.

The inward moving ring then becomes the inward spiral once again and the 3-phase pulse repeats itself over and over.

On the Galaxy Clock, we can see what will happen if we continue with the outward-radiating wave: it will reach the periphery and bounce back and continue its way back to the center in a spiral gravity wave form just like the UFO was dong.

It was astounding evidence to me to suggest that the UFOs were demonstrating the principles of their energy systems and propulsion systems with perfect synchronicity with my new Galaxy Clock and "Gravity Beyond Light Speed Theory." How could the physics of the Galaxy Clock match perfectly with the pulsing waves radiating from the UFOs unless the physics of the Galaxy Clock was an example of the kind of physics the UFOs were utilizing ?

When I studied the very high frequency waves pulsating from the UFOs, I could see the answer to their propulsion system and how they were able to attain and break light speeds. They were pulsing the low frequency mass of their spacecraft (metallic structure) with such high frequency waves, that the frequency of the mass would be raised so high, equal to or greater in frequency than photons, thus reducing their mass to the point that the UFO spacecraft (and every atom it is made of) actually become pure light energy. This is why the UFOs look like pure energy and light rather than solid mass. Once mass becomes as high in frequency as a photon, it can attain the speed of light. Once it goes higher in frequency than a photon, it can also break the speed of light. If we could duplicate their technology, we too could attain the speed of light in a man-woman-made spacecraft.

If we watch the motion of this repeating 3-phase pulse, it looks like an inward collapsing magnetic wave suggesting a gathering of energy. That gathering of energy may be similar to what humans do when they breathe: they gather oxygen for consumption. Once humans have oxygen, they gain energy and use it up. The UFO appears to be gathering some kind of energy and then radiating it out for propulsion, maybe. Could they be gathering the high-energy charged electrons (2.7 MeV electrons) that were discovered by NASA scientists Dr. Louis A. Frank, J.B. Blake and R.S. Selesnick with the Earth camera on the

Polaris satellite? Could a zero-point energy machine work the same way: gathers omnipresent charged particles for fuel?

For my own investigation, I believed that we were seeing the evidence of an extraterrestrial civilization's technology. It was pointing towards our very own possible future. All we had to do was decipher the message.

Further, this all pointed towards the fact that there must be truth to the Zero-Point energy equation and technology. There has reportedly been a great conspiracy against Zero-Point energy machines. Many fear for their lives. The man I was studying with requested that his name not be mentioned in this book for his own protection.

The history of Zero Point energy can best be briefed in the documentary film, "The Race To Zero Point." It details the many great inventors in this field such as Tesla and Morray to modern day Joe Numan, John Hutchison and many more.

Most of these inventors could barely survive. They had little financial support and very little interest from the Department of Energy in Washington, D.C. Joseph Numan has been struggling for decades with the United States Patent office trying to be recognized for a U.S. patent on his invention. So far, no one has commercialized any of the Zero-Point energy technologies because of lack of support. I believed, based on this new evidence, that the Zero-Point energy systems were the movement of future technology for a better environment and for advanced space travel. The UFOs were showing us this plain and clear. My theory proved that to me. I would hope it proves it to the world.

In the year 2000, I was in a bookstore looking for photos of crop circles that may be similar in design to the NASA UFOs. I found a photo of an amazing crop circle formation just 5 months after the STS-75 mission in 1996. The crop circle was formed right across the highway from Stonehenge.

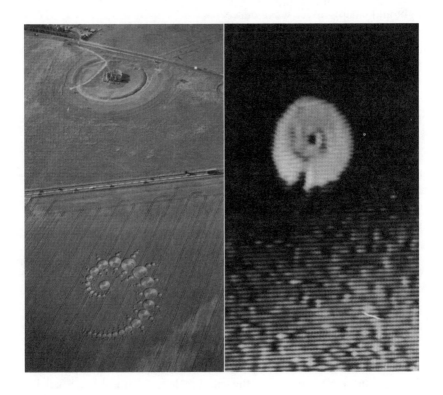

Crop Circle Stonehenge 1996   NASA UFO Gravity Wave 1996

The similarities are astounding. The two gravity waves resemble each other right down to the length of the wave (1.2 spirals) and the frequency of the gravity wave. The frequency of the gravity wave can be measured on the Galaxy Clock from the "Gravity Beyond Light Speed Theory." The frequency of each of these gravity waves can be measured at approximately the 24-count position on the Phase-2 Gravity Clock showing that the UFOs are capable of at least 18.5 times the speed of light. This is in no way certain that the UFOs are not capable of even stronger gravity waves and even faster than 18.5 times the speed of light. But this is what has been demonstrated.

What were the odds that in 1996, these two incidents would reveal an approximate match to the very same frequency of a gravity wave when we consider all of the other frequencies that were possible?

Why didn't one picture show a slow and long curve and the other a tight and steep gravity wave curve?

The similarities were astounding further evidence that this amazing communication was actually taking place between Earth scientists and the ETs.

IV - Sending the New Video Evidence to Dr. Nuth at NASA

I had sent a video copy of the STS-75 tether incident and other new NASA footage mentioned in this book to Dr. Joseph Nuth, III, NASA's head of Astrochemistry at the Goddard Space Flight Center in Greenbelt, Maryland. I wrote him the following letter attached to the video on January 4, 2000:

Subject: NASA STS-75 video tape of "Tether Incident" reveals approximately thirty, 1-3 mile wide circular, anomalous objects flying behind and in front of the satellite and tether. Because the tethered satellite is 70-100 nautical miles away from the space shuttle cameras (the whole 12-mile tether is visible at once), and the anomalous objects pass behind the tether and satellite, they cannot be near field objects or "dust bunnies" in front of the camera lens. The objects can be measured in near approximation against the 12-mile long tether.

Dear Dr. Nuth,

Happy new millennium to you! I have now been in contact with Dr. Louis A. Frank, thanks to you, and have learned a great deal more about his "small comet" hypothesis. He sent me a whole package.

I am temporarily in Canada studying the video library collection of NASA space shuttle missions recorded by a local Cable TV station Program Manager, Martyn Stubbs. I have enclosed for your possible review some footage which I believe answers or challenges many of the questions posed in our prior dialogs.

In your sixth e-mail letter to me of February 22, 1999, you said: "If the phenomenon is interesting enough to deserve and investigation, then our preference would be for controlled experiments that closely duplicate the circumstances or the original observation of the last hypothesis until they are either verified or falsified.

A second line of investigation would be to obtain more evidence of the original sightings (e.g. additional shuttle camera tapes – there are at least four mounted in the bay) to see if the same objects were seen on these. If these objects were large, then the same object should appear on two or more cameras and can be used to triangulate the distance from the shuttle to the object."

On the enclosed videotape, the first segment will show the STS-75 mission, February 25, 1996 following the tether break from the shuttle at approximately 7:30 PM. On the audio portion of the tape, astronauts tell us the tether is 70 and drifting to 100+ nautical miles away from the shuttle. This solves the relativity of distance from the 12-mile tether and satellite and the shuttle. I have studied NASA files on this on the NASA website. I read all about the tether and the experiment.

You will see a swarm of over thirty luminous objects traveling through space and around the tether. Note that they are all travelling at different velocities: some near zero, others several thousand miles per hour (use 12 miles of tether against one second counts of distance) which breaks Galileo's law of gravity: all mass falls through gravity at the same rate regardless of weight, shape, size and density, especially in a vacuum. If these were natural objects falling through space, how could they break this fundamental law? Also, what could cause natural objects to move in such chaotic directions? Notice that none of the anomalous objects collide with each other as one would hypothesize natural objects to do. .

Now, the shuttle video camera pans down and zooms in to get a closer look at these anomalies. They can now be seen to have clear, circular shape with obvious portals (square shaped openings). They all clearly pass behind the tether and satellite. This confirms that they are equal or greater than the same distance between the shuttle (cameras) and the tethered satellite (70-100 nautical miles). Therefore, they are not near field objects or dust bunnies in the shuttle environment. Assuming the largest of the objects is within a small distance behind the tether, we can measure their minimum size to be a titanic 1-3 miles in diameter. This is astounding Dr. Nuth! What do you think?

Also, try replaying the tape and only focus your eyes on the portals and you will notice that they appear on one side of the nearly perfect circles and then move to the other side. Also, a few of these objects have waves of pulsating energy it seems. What peculiarities these anomalies have. Could the waves be propulsion energy?

The second incident on the enclosed tape is what I call the manifestation sequence. It shows many luminous objects flying about. Some streak and incredible speeds and some very slow. Then we see, in the upper middle of the screen, a disc shaped object suddenly manifest as if coming from another dimension. We then see a bright streak moving away from the earth's gravity at tremendous speed. What do you think?

The third sequence on this tape is what I call the formation, while the shuttle is passing over Southern Africa. It shows a number of lights gathering in a circle. It takes some time to form this circle. We then see a circular, low density, almost transparent object pass by in the near field towards the circle in the background and enter the center of the circle. It lights up when it reaches the very center of the circle. This shows intelligence and timing that one would not expect to find in natural objects, including ejected junk from the shuttle. What do you think?

The fourth scene on this tape I have sent you before. It reveals something I have missed until just yesterday. While we see a high-speed left angle turn going on in the space above the earth, in the lower space above the earth below, we can see a small shooting star-like object which moves very quickly in a curved fashion relative to the curvature of the earth. It then disappears exactly when it reaches the horizon of the earth indicating that it was travelling in the relatively low space above the earth and circling the globe. Because it moves in such a fashion that is relative to the curvature of the earth eliminates the possibility of the object being in the near field of the camera. This is my own analysis. What do you think?

Now, assuming that the object moved over a very conservative estimate of 1,000 miles of the earth's surface in four seconds (I counted and used maps for distances), the object would have to be travelling at 250 miles per second.

This comes to an astounding 900,000 mph, a speed that far surpasses any natural object, aircraft or spacecraft ever recorded. I really believe it may have traveled over some 2,000 miles of the earth's surface in the four seconds I counted giving it a speed of 1.8 million mph. The energy required for such velocities could only be attained using nuclear propulsions systems.

When I talked to Earl Van Landingham, Director of Propulsion, Power and Energy at NASA some years ago about NASA's possible involvement in Dr. Bogdan Maglich's Aneutronic fusion reactor, he said he was interested in using the reactor as a lightweight power source and a nuclear propulsion system. He said at the University of Wisconsin at Madison, they were doing research into utilizing anti-protons for space propulsion. For example, he said that using Maglich's fusion reactor with a successful deuterium+helium-3 fusion, the energy would be between 17-18 MeV. 17-18 MeV protons could enable spacecraft to do $1/10^{th}$ the speed of light. Maglich never got funding. Even James Fletcher, a friend of Maglich's was turned down by the Reagan administration when he asked for funding to complete Maglich's work.

Nuclear propulsion systems were successfully tested by EG&G at the Nuclear Rocket station in Nevada in 1968. It is on their website under their history section at www.egginc.com.

My question to you is, are some of the objects we are seeing on this tape advanced propulsion and space vehicle tests? What else could approach 1 million mph?

After you review this tape, would you consider a deeper investigation at NASA into such unexplainable physics of movement and objects of such enormous size, such as in the STS-75 tether incident?

I await for your reply either by e-mail or regular mail.

Sincerely,

David Sereda

I knew that I had NASA in "checkmate."
I had too much evidence, not all of which did I share with Dr. Nuth right away, to prove that these objects were not space debris, meteors, shooting stars, or "dust bunnies" or even "ice crystals" for that matter. I waited a long time. He did not want to answer me. Dr. Nuth was usually prompt. I wrote him the following e-mail letter on January 28, 2000:

Dear Dr. Nuth,

I hope you received my package of the new NASA video footage. I realize the STS-75 tether incident is very difficult to explain as well as some other incidents. I have studied it on NASA's website. While I am aware of the purpose of that experiment, and have consulted with other physicists about it, I will await your possible answers.

I already knew he was scared and his immediate answer to me proved it. He wrote me the following letter on January 29, 2000:

Dear Mr. Sereda,

I received your package but other duties have kept me from watching the tape you sent. I must admit that I am somewhat reluctant to begin another dialog with you on this subject, as

186

our last discussion nearly resulted in a formal Freedom of Information Act request on an area in which I have no formal responsibility or specialized NASA knowledge. I do not mind responding to inquiries from the public since I feel that this is part of my job as a government employee. However, I really have little interest in getting into battles when my honest attempts to answer your questions do not seem to agree with what you want me to say. My personal (home) vcr has been broken for a while and I have not yet had time to borrow one. When I do, I will let you know what I think that I see in the tape.
Joe Nuth

The Freedom of Information Act request didn't stop Nuth from continuing to speak with me in the past. In fact, we both expressed a sense of humor about it. His response letter (signed and mailed to me) about my FOIA request was written on February 24, 1999. The very next day, February 25, 1999, Dr. Nuth wrote me an invitation letter to attend a NASA workshop on the Leonid meteors to show the tape in person at the SETI institute in Mountainview, California on March 1, 1999. Dr. Nuth wrote me the following letter:

Dear Mr. Sereda,

I am forwarding this in hope that you might be able to attend and because the meeting should be attended by many people most knowledgeable about meteors. This should be a place where you can find someone to answer most of your questions in person.

Joe Nuth

The purpose of the workshop is to review the first results of the 1998 Leonid campaigns, both ground-based and airborne campaigns, discuss the relevant science, and make recommendations for the upcoming campaigns in November 1999.

Researchers from the fields of meteor physics, atmospheric science, planetary astronomy, and astrobiology are invited to attend, as well as those concerned with the satellite impact hazard of meteor storms. The meeting is open to amateurs.

We anticipate an exciting 3-day meeting that is very interdisciplinary in nature and that will set the stage for the organization of next year's campaigns, our last chance to witness a meteor storm in our lifetime.

Sincerely,
Dr. Peter Jenniskens

A very friendly gesture like this did not suggest the end of a great dialogue between two individuals. It was a great opportunity for me to meet these people in person and show the tape. I felt the risk was too high for them to know all that I had and to know my face. Also, I knew that the objects in the tape were not meteors. I didn't need an expert to try and convince me that a meteor cannot survive for distances longer than a few seconds and that the alleged meteors (shooting stars) in the NASA video never burned out as meteors do when they are small. As we already investigated, only large meteors do not burn out but large meteors create enormous explosions upon impact with the Earth, so much that they can destroy life. Because no major explosions that destroyed massive amounts of life on Earth happened in the 1990s, I knew they were not meteors.

In this last letter from Dr. Nuth, he not only didn't claim to see the video, he avoided all of my questions.

The evidence that the UFOs were passing "behind" a tethered satellite 77-100 nautical miles away from the cameras on the shuttle Columbia was empirical and clear in proving that the UFOs were not anything near the cameras, therefore actual UFOs. Other evidence already mentioned was also stunning. He knew it, I thought, and avoided me on purpose by saying that his vcr was broken. As if NASA didn't have a vcr.

I sent the photographs of the 3-phase pulse to Dr. Joseph Nuth and wrote him the following letter on January 22, 2000:

Dear Dr. Nuth,

I just wanted to see if you received the photos from the NASA video I sent you? Also, have you seen the video tape yet? What do you think of the pulsing waves of light and their peculiar formations?

Dr. Nuth wrote me back the following letter on February 22, 2000:

Dear Mr. Sereda,

Yes, I received your photographs and they are indeed quite peculiar. However, at least in the photographs, I have seen nothing that could not be explained as floating debris illuminated through sharp shadows in the shuttle bay (maybe the videotape show different things). I will try to see the tape soon.

Joe Nuth

This was amazing. Dr. Nuth just would not accept the clear and simple facts that the tether is 77-100 miles away from the shuttle and its cameras and that the UFOs pass "behind" the tether. They are not in the shuttle bay. Considering this, he does say the photos "are indeed quite peculiar." That is saying a lot for NASA. "Quite peculiar" was his answer and now he was supposed to see the video and get back to me.

The next thing I did was to send Dr. Nuth my "Gravity Beyond Light Speed Theory" with the photos again and see if he would answer to that. I sent the package off on March 7, 2000 and waited for an answer.

V – NASA's Breakthrough Propulsion Physics Program

NASA developed a new program for research into new ideas for energy and advanced propulsions systems in 1996, the same year of the STS-75 "Tether Incident." NASA's new goal is to seek ultimate breakthroughs in space transportation as follows:

1) Propulsion systems that require no propellant mass. That means no fuel;

2) Propulsion systems that attain maximum transit speeds physically possible;

3) Breakthrough methods of energy production to power such devices.

The topics of interest to this new program include experiments and theories regarding coupling of gravity and electromagnetism, the quantum vacuum, hyper-fast travel, and superluminal quantum effects. Because the propulsion goals are presumably far from fruition, a special emphasis in the program is towards identifying affordable, near-term, and credible research that could make measurable progress towards these propulsion goals.

The program is managed by Dr. Marc G. Millis at the NASA Glenn Research Center in Cleveland, Ohio.

Why did NASA suddenly decide in 1996 that quantum ideas in space travel were feasible? Why was there a sudden race to get to the quantum technology when previously such ideas were considered impossible and against the laws of physics, presumably Einstein's theory that the mass of a spacecraft cannot attain light speed? Did NASA realize the same phenomenon in quantum physics that I did when they studied the STS-75 "Tether Incident" in their sequestered meetings?

What NASA was also saying here was that it is interested in Zero-Point energy research, "experiments and theories in the quantum vacuum" and that they knew the only way to attain such a vacuum is by creating a gravity generator by "electromagnetism." These are the same ideas being researched by the outcast Zero-Point energy researchers.

In 1999, NASA's Breakthrough Propulsion Physics Program selected Jordan Maclay of Quantum Fields LLC of Richland Center, Wisconsin and MEMS Optical in Huntsville, Alabama to propose an experimental and theoretical study of quantum vacuum energy (essentially Zero-Point energy). The experiments will use microelectromechanical devices to test force and energy effects predicted by quantum electrodynamics. Another five projects were also chosen for research, including faster than light speed research.

The program stated that "The distances between stars is so great that with existing propulsion technology a probe would travel tens of thousands of years before reaching our nearest neighboring star. Even with the most ambitious new propulsion technology based on known physics, it would still be extremely difficult for a probe to reach that far within fifty years. To overcome these limitations to practical interstellar space travel, new propulsion physics is being sought by the Breakthrough Propulsion Physics Program."

NASA clearly stated in this new program that they knew that for a spacecraft to travel at hyper-fast speeds, it would have to rely on an energy source that is beyond all rocket and propulsion systems requiring fuels. This is because there is a maximum speed that a propulsion system can deliver for a spacecraft using fuels and that is far from light speed.

In an article in "Popular Science" magazine in November, 1999, entitled "Plasma Propulsion – Charged Particle Engines Blast Off for the Outer Planets," the same program receives public relations at the NASA Glenn Research Center, but void of its new quantum ideas. Here, NASA is informing the public of its new "Plasma Propulsion" systems, which still use propellant. The first plasma drives were built at the NASA Glenn Research Center back in 1958. Edgar Choueiri heads the lab there for plasma drive research.

Plasma propulsion uses a mixture of fuel and electricity to supercharge the fuel. Using electricity to create high-energy plasma, the new propulsion systems still fall a long way short of near light speed and beyond ideas that are detailed in NASA's Breakthrough Propulsion Physics Program. Supercharging fuel (plasma) is a great idea, but we still need an electrical energy source on the spacecraft to charge the fuel and we till need fuel. If you run out of one or both, the spacecraft dies. This is the biggest problem the research has encountered. So far, all sources of electrical power that remains safe are less than 100 kilowatts. That is not a lot of power. Alternatives like nuclear power leave fears of radiation to astronauts.

Mysteriously, one of the leaders in plasma drive propulsion systems is Dr. Franklin Chang-Diaz, the very astronaut who flew on the STS-75 space shuttle mission and commented live on the UFOs calling them, "Debris illuminated by the sun at such low angles" and "there's a lot of stray light and things are getting washed out." Dr. Chang-Diaz is the head of NASA's Advanced Space Propulsion Laboratory at the Johnson Space Flight Center in Houston, Texas. His new concept in space propulsion is among the most hopeful of all projects in development at NASA.

If we remember that the STS-75 "Tether Incident" UFOs were "pulsing" with energy waves, or what I call gravity-stronger-than-light-speed-waves, the thesis for Dr. Chang Diaz's research appears all to familiar. He is developing a Variable Specific Impulse Magnetoplasma Rocket (VSIMR) that utilizes "pulsed radio frequency electromagnetic waves" of energy.

The keywords in his design are "pulsed" and "electromagnetic waves." Does this sound familiar? If scientists like Dr. Chang-Diaz was witnessing UFOs on the STS-75 mission and saw that they were pulsing with electromagnetic waves of energy, he might get his own ideas about trying to learn from these allegedly extraterrestrial spacecraft. Could Dr. Franklin Chang-Diaz have reverse-engineered this new technology of his based on observations he made during the STS-75 and previous missions? He is a veteran of six space shuttle missions.

I researched Dr. Chang-Diaz's inventions at the U.S. Patent office website. I found that he had one patent (U.S. Patent # 4,93,470) granted on June 16, 1990. It was a method of hybrid plume plasma propulsion. It did not involve a pulsed magnetic wave. He didn't develop that until after 1996 it seemed, after he witnessed the pulsing UFOs.

Dr. Franklin Chang-Diaz may have seen UFOs on many other missions. He is a veteran of six flights: STS-61-C in 1986, STS-34 in 1989, STS-46 in 1992, STS-60 in 1994, STS-75 (the "Tether Incident" mission) in 1996 and STS-91 in 1998. His earliest mission in 1986 precedes his earliest patented propulsion invention in 1990.

I cannot prove that Dr. Chang-Diaz got his ideas from these UFOs, but I can hypothesize that it was a great possibility that they inspired his research. Nevertheless, I don't think he is going in the same direction as the quantum technology that these UFOs are using.

Dr. Chang-Diaz oversees several development stages that may lead to the first manned mission to Mars in 2018. How did this Costa Rican born physicist/astronaut become the head of such research at NASA? Did NASA heads appoint him because he understood the observations he made on the STS-75 mission? Certainly a pulsed plasma rocket is still a long way away from reaching light speed and the quantum goals of the NASA Breakthrough Propulsion Physics Program.

Dr. Chang-Diaz's VSIMR engine hopes to utilize a 100-kilowatt power source, which is not enough power to do even the $1/10^{th}$ the speed of light that Dr. Bogdan Maglich's deuterium-helim-3 miniature fusion reactor would have been capable of delivering. The United States Air Force findings on Super Cray II computer simulations showed that this reactor could have produced a billion watts of continuous electrical power.

If we compare Dr. Maglich's billion watts of power to Dr. Chang-Diaz's 100 kilowatts, NASA seems far behind. As Dr. Earl VanLandingham, then NASA Director of Propulsion, Power and Energy stated to me, "The 18 MeV charged protons in Dr. Maglich's miniature fusion reactor could enable spacecraft to do $1/10^{th}$ the speed of light."

But why did NASA abort its chance to fund the technology for a billion-watt space power source when today its goals appear to be in need of such technology? Could decisions in Washington be unwise? Or, was it Congress that aborted the research into Maglich's technology because it was privy to information on the alternative space program research? No one really knows the answers to these questions except for those persons sequestered in the Department of Defense and Congress.

The only thing we do know is the astronauts who flew on that fateful mission, including Dr. Franklin Chang-Diaz, know the truth about what they saw that day of February 25, 1996 after the tether broke at 7:00 P.M.

I wrote a letter to Dr. Chang Diaz, sending him a copy of the video of the STS-75 mission UFOs. I told him I didn't believe his statements that these were caused by "stray light" or that they were caused by "debris being illuminated by the sun at such low angles." I also gave him an earlier version of my "Gravity Beyond Light Speed Theory" and the pictures of the 3-phase gravity wave pulse.

I did not receive a single answer from Dr. Chang-Diaz. Once I telephoned his office and left him a message to call me. I wanted to go to the Lion's den to get the answers from the Lion's mouth. Still, I did not even get a reply that suggested his own theories or a rebuttal of my observations.

VI - THE INTER-DIMENSIONAL SHIFT SEQUENCE

The next sequence on the Martyn Stubbs, NASA video involves an alleged UFO manifesting from an invisible dimension to one that is visible to the human eye (or video camera with iridium filters to see in the UV range). Now that the notion of other dimensions has been investigated and proven using radiated energy spectroscopy (light in different radiation levels), it will be easier to understand what we are seeing in this sequence of the video.

Watching the Martyn Stubbs, NASA video, we see that the space shuttle is over North West Africa. We see lightning strikes on the ground. There is a thunder and lightning storm in Africa. A disc-shaped object moves from the lower right side of the screen into and across the center. It looks like a familiar UFO. Other mysterious objects appear to gather around. They all travel at different speeds. A few very fast moving objects speed by, some in a flash or streak of light. They are clearly leaving Earth's atmosphere and escaping Earth's gravity. They cannot be meteors and must have internal energy. They do not appear to be low in altitude relative to the altitude of the space shuttle. One object shoots straight down into the Earth and disappears into the clouds below. Meteors do not shoot straight down into the Earth. They glide in at an angle relative to gravity (curved).

Suddenly, in the upper center of the screen, a large disc-shaped light manifests in a split second as if from another dimension. It looks identical to the objects seen flying behind the tether in the

STS-75 mission "tether incident." The object than flies slowly off to the left position and moves down towards the earth but stays at a high altitude. This is incredible.

Now, we can see a small circle of lights gathering on the lower left of the screen showing intelligence and architecture once again. On the lower right of the screen, we can see three or four objects (lights) forming a triangle. The space shuttle camera zooms in on the triangle formation. The cameras look at this for a while then zoom back out.

It is important to clarify a scientific matter for the investigation to go to the next level presented here. The ORFEUS SPAS-2 satellite will look at stars and other celestial objects in the far and extreme ultraviolet range of light (radiant energy). Stars emit light in the full spectrum if radio waves, infrared light, visible light, ultraviolet light (near, far and extreme), x-ray and gamma rays and more. Radio telescopes, like those used by the SETI (Search For Extraterrestrial Intelligence) Institute in Mountainview, California, can take radio pictures of stars. Infrared satellite cameras and telescopes can also take pictures of stars. Visible light cameras and telescopes can take pictures of stars. UV cameras and telescopes, like the ones used on the ORFEUS SPAS-2 satellite can also take pictures of stars. Each of these cameras will see a different picture of the same star because each of them is photographing a different frequency of the light energy radiating from the star.

For an object to only be visible in a limited range of light energy frequency is an incredible discovery. This is because it suggests either inter-dimensionality or alter-dimensionality of the object being observed. This is the case for the discovery of Dr. Louis A. Frank's alleged "small comets." They are only visible in the UV range so far as detected.

If the video camera used on this space shuttle mission could see objects that were only visible in the UV range, and objects that had residual light reflected in the UV range, and we saw an object manifest from a higher dimension of radiated energy, where would it have come from? The object could not have had light in the visible range prior to manifesting. It would have either had to have previously been in a lower dimension of light energy (infrared or radio wave) or a higher dimension of light energy (extreme or far UV, x-rays, gamma rays or higher).

The sudden appearance of this mysterious, disc-shaped object (UFO) suggests inter-dimensionality. A star cannot do this. That is because a star is always emitting light in the full spectrum of radiant energy. A star will always show up on a camera and film sensitive to any of the known spectrums of radiant energy.

What we have just witnessed on the Martyn Stubbs, NASA video may be actual proof of an inter-dimensional shift of an extraterrestrial spacecraft or living entity. It is an amazing sight to see.

VII - SIGNAL FROM PEGASUS INCIDENT

In November of 1998, the "Art Bell" radio show hosted guest Richard C. Hoagland, former science advisor to "Walter Cronkite," founder of "The Mars Investigation Group," and founder of "The Enterprise Mission." Hoagland is well known for his space sciences and mystical research into ancient civilizations. Hoagland was now on the radio talking about an alleged radio signal detected from the star EQ Pegasus. The signal, Hoagland and associates calculated, was decelerating in energy (as radio waves are energy) and would reach a velocity of "zero" at the moment the signal would arrive at Earth on December 7, 1998. This made Hoagland and his associates feel that the signal from the EQ Pegasus star system was being intelligently sent to Earth.

Hoagland was convinced something miraculous would happen when the full strength of the Signal reached Earth. It was the first intelligent communication from another star system ever recorded. It was all too familiar to the Hollywood movie "Contact," based on the late astrophysicist Carl Sagan's book, "Contact." Dr. Sagan predicted that one day Earth would receive an intelligent signal detected by radio telescopes. The signal would yield extraterrestrial contact. Our national leaders and military would involve themselves in the unprecedented event. While it didn't appear as though the public at large (other than Art Bell fans) nor the military and international leaders became involved in the signal from Pegasus, Hoagland and his associates took the signal very seriously. Fans from all over the world anxiously awaited December 7, 1998.

Hoagland's group found their evidence in early December when giant circles suddenly started appearing in weather satellite pictures on national radar. "Accuweather," an American satellite weather station and website hosted photographs of the mysterious circles appearing on their maps. While Accuweather didn't know exactly why the circles were appearing (perhaps due to a computer glitch) on their weather maps, Hoagland and his associates were almost certain that this had something to do with the signal from the star EQ Pegasus. The timing was nearly impeccable. Throughout the week of December 2nd through the 12th, giant circles started appearing all over the United States. Perhaps they were appearing in other countries at the same time, but Accuweather only showed satellite photos of The United States and Canada.

On December 2nd, 1998 at 3:30 PM Eastern time, a large circle was detected and was moving over the state of Nothern Idaho and into Montana. The fact that the circle was moving was stunning. The circle would be estimated to be nearly 200 miles in diameter. What did all of this mean to Richard Hoagland and his associates?

By December 5, 1998, Hoagland and his associates put all of their focus on a large circle appearing in Arizona. He and his group felt that this may have been the center of the signal from Pegasus' origin, or its destination for arrival. The center of the signal was at Turret Peak in Arizona. Researchers drove in their vehicles to the top of Turret Peak on the evening of December 7, 1998 to see if a giant space ship would arrive. After a long night of researchers having vehicle problems and getting stranded, nothing unusual had occurred. There was terrible weather all over the mountain. Hoagland even suggested that Electric Low Frequency (ELF) energy was responsible for the weather (weather control technology) just to keep people away. Hoagland's associates found and ELF signal coming from the mountain that very night. But what was causing the signal?

For the next few days, giant circles appeared over Texas, the eastern United States and even California and then vanished. The December 7 day had passed. Hoagand and his associates felt that the whole EQ Pegasus signal may have been a hoax perpetrated by military. He alleged that the military was using ELF waves to control the weather. But did he miss something?

After studying the Martyn Stubbs, NASA video, our research pointed into an amazing parallel. The giant 2-3 mile wide circles (UFOs) that appeared during the February, 1996, STS-75 "Tether Incident," and the "Inter-Dimensional-Shift sequence we had just investigated all pointed to the Pegasus incident with a new, hypothetical perspective.

We had already investigated how visible light is only a small part of the radiant energy spectrum. We saw giant circular objects travelling around the STS-75 tethered satellite that may have only been visible using ultraviolet-light-sensitive filters on the space shuttle's video camera. We also saw a large disc-shaped object (UFO) suddenly manifest from another (invisible) dimension of energy. We had investigated the discovery of Dr. Louis A. Frank's alleged "small comets" (circular-shaped objects only visible on UV cameras), with NASA's head of Astrochemistry, Dr. Jospeh Nuth, III. This was all pointing to large circles that were invisible to the human eye because the human eye can only see a small part of the total radiant energy spectrum.

The new hypothesis about the EQ Pegasus signal now becomes crystal clear. What if there really was an intelligent radio signal from the star system EQ Pegasus? What if that signal involved enormous "Mother-Ships" (UFOs) that were inter-dimensional craft. Because they traveled from Pegasus to Earth with such great speed, they had to be high-energy craft with an atomic structure relevant to their ability to travel beyond or at light speed. Their signal could be found utilizing radar because radar sees signals in the form of energy.

Our research group had a new theory: Inter-dimensional craft were being detected on NASA space shuttle missions and perhaps on Earth. The means for detection of these "Independence Day" sized craft was detection systems sensitive to radiant energy waves. What if Earth was visited by extraterrestrials during NASA space shuttle missions and during the December 7, 1998 EQ Pegasus incident and we keep thinking that extraterrestrials are supposed to manifest right in front of our eyes at the same frequency where we see energy: the as the discs seen on the NASA video of the STS-75 "Tether Incident" (larger than a downtown core of a major city); and 200 miles in diameter, such as the giant circles on the Accuweather maps, were to manifest in the visible light spectrum, how would we react?

Would international governments and militaries align themselves to form one global superpower? President Ronald Reagan spoke at a United Nations assembly hypothesizing such an invasion by stating, "I often wonder how quickly our differences would dissolve if we were suddenly faced with an alien threat from outside this world." Did Reagan have access to NASA's discoveries? Does he know what is happening at "Area-51" in Nevada? Why is he telling the United Nation's assembly this?

Considering what Reagan said, we know that we would react in a military fashion, possibly united all over the world. If the extraterrestrial spacecraft of the sizes mentioned in this investigation were to manifest in the visible light spectrum of human beings, the response would most likely not be friendly. Is this why these craft remain detectable, but invisible to this dimension? Will these ultra-advanced civilizations wait for us to recognize their arrival and that it has already happened? Do they remain safe from military attack while manifest in alternate, parallel dimensions but vulnerable if they manifest in our dimension? Are the numerous, random sightings of UFOs caused when their craft temporarily jump from an invisible dimension into our own? Based on what I had seen with my own eyes in Berkeley, California, in 1968, and the evidence presented in the NASA video "Inter-Dimensional Shift Sequence," I am convinced that this is what was happening.

There was more evidence from the International Space Initiative to suggest the existence extremely large spacecraft (Motherships). In 1988, The Russians, in an international effort, launched two space probes on a mission to Mars called "Phobos I and II. Phobos I was launched on July 7, 1998. After 53 days, all contact with the probe was alleged to be lost. The Phobos II probe was launched on July 10, 1988. It was a successful mission.

Reported in the foreign press and news, the Phobos II satellite had taken photos some 60,000 kilometers above the surface of Mars revealing a long (hundreds of miles) elliptical shadow on the ground. The shape of the shadow was not like that of the Mars moon also named Phobos. The Mars moonlet was an amorphous shape. There was also no eclipse between the Phobos moonlet of Mars and the sun to have caused the shadow. Researchers who studied the photos of the mysterious shadow then reported that it was moving. The shape of the shadow was that of a disc on its side. What could it have been? The shadow moved and then disappeared.

Reported by the British News Media, was the fact that shortly after the shadow had disappeared from the surface of Mars, whatever had made the shadow was moving towards the Phobos II satellite. The Russians had apparently taken two photos of the mysterious alleged UFO and then all contact with the Phobos II satellite was lost. The Russians would not share the photos with international interests. They remained sequestered in Russia.

There are only a few possibilities as to what may have caused the shadow. It couldn't have been another planet. It couldn't have been the Mars moon. If it were a meteorite, it would have most likely impacted with Mars and the explosion would have been clearly visible from Earth. It wasn't a meteorite. For now, it will be called an unidentified disc-shaped object (UFO).

VIII – Quantum Phenomena

Martyn Stubbs had recorded a lot of other mysterious phenomenon on the space shuttle missions. We saw on the tape a UFO speeding up to the space shuttle and then curving back out into space at high-speed. We saw many brightly glowing objects in full color leaving the Earth's atmosphere. We saw many objects perform phenomenal maneuvers, but Martyn still had a mad smile on his face. He had saved his best discovery for last.

Just as subatomic nuclear particle physicists like Luis Alvarez, Murray Gell-Mann and Bogdan Maglich have to search deeply for new particles and theories in physics, Martyn had to search deeply behind the video technology to find his superfluous phenomenal UFOs.

To an average observer, Martyn's phenomena would go by like a fleck of paint hitting a windshield at 145 miles per hour. No one would notice. But subatomic particle physicists search for flecks of paint in the deep recesses of subatomic matter.

Just as subatomic particle physicist smashes particles for their deeper nature, Martyn Stubbs took apart the split frames of sections of the NASA video looking for his inter-dimensional UFOs. The type of video camera on the shuttle at the time of these missions used a spilt-frame technology that scanned horizontal lines at high resolution in two frames that are joined together to make up a complete frame.

When Martyn took apart the split frames, he found something amazing. Sudden streaks of colored lights appeared on one side of the split frame and the amazing phenomena was that the streaks of color did not appear on the very next frame suggesting that they had made the same quantum leap that electrons make and "red shifts" make. They appeared but did not pass through the intervening space to make their appearance. If they had been traveling through the intervening space, they would have shown up on the next frame in the next progressive position of their line of trajectory. They did not show up anywhere else.

The answer to Martyn's mysterious phenomenon baffled him to no end. I didn't have the answer until the year 2000 when I had made my discovery of the "Gravity Beyond Light Speed Theory" and had researched Zero-Point energy.

Martyn's new discovery was a perfect match to the "quantum leap" that was so unexplainable to moderns science caught in viewing the universe in relative light speed time. My theory about this phenomenon was clear: that these UFOs or even highly charged particles were skipping across different frequencies of gravity waves. When one of these UFOs or charged particles jumped from a gravity wave frequency beyond light speed, it would disappear from the cameras that view objects in relative light speed time. When the UFO or charged particle slowed down to the frequency of relative light speed time, the camera would see it while it remained in that frequency.

The fact that these UFOs or charged particles were jumping so quickly into our dimension of relative light speed time and back out suggested to me that this was further scientific proof that these different frequencies of gravity existed and that charged particles represented the energy that flowed from one frequency to another. UFOs could do the same thing. They could appear to make the quantum leap from this dimension into the next because they were utilizing quantum energy technologies.

Other dimensions are now explained simply as dimensions where the atomic state of matter is vibrating above or below the frequency of the dimension we now see and hear.

To find out what life is like in these other dimensions, we would have to expand our technology base by learning from these examples and take the giant quantum leap ourselves.
We would have to get out of the fossil fuel burning age and expand into electrodynamic electrical power generation like the suppressed Zero-Point energy inventors have been trying to do for decades. If we did this, we might even see the end to the pollution and destruction to the environment caused by energy residue pollution.

Chapter Seven
Antagonism

"A Fanatic is one who can't change his mind and will not change the subject" - Winston Churchill

I – Astronomers in High Places

In 1999, Martyn Stubbs offered his tape to a group in England (Graham Birdsall and Russell Callahan) who presented their interpretation of his findings at the February, 2000 International UFO Congress in Laughlin, Nevada. I was not impressed with Martyn's ideas of letting this whole thing get out into the public before I was finished my clandestine investigations in the scientific community. What followed was a disaster to the working relationship between Martyn Stubbs, the group from England, Mike Boyle and myself. The English group published information about the NASA video and broadcast excerpts from it live on the internet in early 2000. I was outraged. The English group called the project, "The Smoking Gun," thinking they had caught NASA dead in its tracks with solid evidence.

Clare Williams, Head Astronomer & Planetarium Manager of the Canberra Space Dome & Observatory in Australia replied to group from England after she had seen a copy of the Martyn Stubbs NASA video (the Smoking Gun), march 29, 2000:

I've had a quick look at the NASA "smoking gun" tape. As far as the footage is concerned. Here are my thoughts so far. There won't be an awful lot that is new to you in what I have say, but you can pass this on to UFO MAGAZINE and fellow researchers.

1991 Mir Volkov Krikaliov footage:

The footage appears to have been taken with a handheld camera.
It shows a pinpoint light source, which appears to be moving with a

smooth trajectory against the backdrop of the Earth. The object is tracked as it moves in front of the Earth's surface. The object appears to be in orbit below the Mir. At times, the cameraman zooms in to the object which takes on the appearance of a 'fuzzy' disk. During the zoom sequences, the object appears to 'jump around'. This motion is consistent with it being a handheld camera and has nothing to do with the motion of the object itself. The disk-like appearance is consistent with this being a pinpoint light source which is still below the camera's resolution. I have to say that I got the distinct impression that this footage was taken in anticipation of the object appearing, rather than just being some random filming, but this may be subjective as the footage is taken out of context and I have no idea what the original purpose of this footage might have been. The appearance and motion of the object is consistent with that of a satellite being illuminated by the sun. I was struck by the thought that this might have been the space shuttle. A Mir cosmonaut might very well want to record the passage of the shuttle as it orbited below the space station and he would have been expecting it to appear. If it is not the shuttle, in the footage, then I see nothing in the footage to suggest to me that this is anything other than one of dozens of satellites in low Earth orbit.

The tether footage:

The objects in the tether footage are clearly in the near foreground and not, as claimed by Stubbs and others, at the distance of the tether itself. This is apparent when one looks carefully at how they change in appearance when the focus of the camera is shifted.

When we first see the objects, they appear as a swarm of randomly moving bright dots. The tether in a bright 'rod-like' object in the distance. The shuttle astronaut is trying to adjust the focus and contrast of the camera. As he shifts the focus to infinity (the setting one would use for an object at the distance of the tether), faint stars become visible moving in the background (the shuttle and tether are in orbit and moving at several thousand kms per hour so the stars appear to move). At this time, the 'swarming' objects in the field turn into Airy disks (out of focus point sources of light). Many show the dark "bullseye" center that is characteristic of an Airy disk. The tether is in focus as well as it can be at this stage, as are the stars which is what one would expect considering its distance (some 70 kms). The swarming objects are not, which means that they cannot be at the same distance as the tether. They are actually in the foreground and are probably no more than a few meters away from the camera.

This is proven by the fact that as the focus shifts back to the foreground, the background stars become harder to see, while the swarming objects become sharper and brighter. There is a good deal of difference between the two focus settings, which means that there must also be a good deal of distance. The astronaut cameraman is having difficulty finding a good focus and contrast setting and is actually focused on the foreground when he says that he can't get it any better than that.

As an aside, the tether was surprisingly highly reflective and was actually visible from the ground. If these UFOs were large objects near the tether, they should also have been visible to observers on the ground. I don't know of anyone who reported them although plenty of people reported observing the tether itself.

This is another example of people not being able to tell the difference between out of focus images and in focus images. Because the Airy disk appears to have a well defined edge and nice circular shape, people mistakenly think the object is in focus, when in actuality, it is as out of focus as it can get. Anyone with a video camera or binoculars or telescope can prove this for themselves by simply going out and playing with the focus while the instrument is looking at a point source of light, such as a star or distant streetlight - something you know is not a UFO! An in focus star should appear as a pinpoint or as near to a pinpoint as you can get. As the focus is shifted, the light from the star becomes spread out across the focal plane and we see the Airy disk. The Airy disk is a familiar sight to optical astronomers and a telltale indicator to those who can recognize it for what it actually is. Airy disks are not merely a property of stars. Any point source of light will show one.

The door scene - another space phenomena?

I also had an opportunity to run the 'door' scene through frame by frame and I think the 'space phenomena' discussed here must be the little flashes which show up looking like tiny comets. These are most likely due to cosmic rays striking the camera's CCD chip. Cosmic rays often show up in images from orbiting instruments. The SOHO data, for example, is full of them. I recently learned that astronauts often experience these as bright flashes of light and that initially surprised me. They were thoroughly investigated during the Apollo program as they were a bit of a mystery and it was considered that they might pose a health hazard with prolonged exposure.

A word on Airy disks:

I think it's only fair to clarify what an Airy disk is. It is what you get when a pinpoint light source is out of focus. It looks like a bright circle, or sphere, sometimes with a dark bit like a Bullseye in the middle or concentric rings. These are interference patterns due to the wave nature of light. If you want to take a look at one, then check out the object in question in the STS80 (or is it STS60, I've seen it referred to as both) footage. If you understand what you're looking at, then you can tell if the object was inside the camera's focus or outside. This can tell you if the object was close to the camera or far away.

I was appalled to see in an interview with Jack Kasher on the STS80(60?) footage ("Confirmation" USA-TV'99) that he failed to recognise what was clearly an Airy disk when he saw one. Not only that, but the Airy disk tells me that the object was close to the camera - inside the focus and probably only a few feet away - rather than far away. I don't mean to sound defamatory, but Dr Kasher doesn't seem all that familiar with the behaviour of light in optical systems. This led him to make an incorrect assumption about the distance of the objects in the STS48 footage and is a fatal flaw in that analysis.

We also have objects that are referred to as spheres that would be more accurately described as 'fuzzy dots'. Mostly we see these in images that are either nearing or at the limit of the cameras zoom function. These objects actually have quite small apparent diameters and the image may only actually be a few pixels across - not enough to make out any shape or detail, but on zoom, the image along with any motion or aberrations in the camera's optical system are magnified. This frequently removes the image from its context and makes it difficult to determine what's actually going on.

Worse still camcorders have a very nasty habit of going out of focus when the zoom function is engaged on a pinpoint light source. We don't always get the bullseye effect, however. Sometimes the centre can be brighter and this can make it look like a metallic sphere. Sorry if this is turning into a lesson in optics, but this is important. Once you know what to look for and become familiar with it, these things become instantly recognisable to you. I think most of the so-called 'spheres' are Airy disks.

With CCD chips a bright point of light often appears to have a "dark" or shadowed side, which is actually an artefact of the charge on the chip. This enhances the metallic sphere illusion even more, but even a star or planet will show this effect. It is an effect which is quite pronounced on the Panasonic video cameras we use in our observatory, so I recognise it quite readily. I've seen it on shuttle footage as well. I will eventually put all of this stuff in a paper on my own website: www.cfmeu.asn.au/cwilliams

Here are some other thoughts as taken from my correspondence on the matter with Charlene Ballam:

These 'objects' that have generated so much controversy and excitement are, if you understand anything about optics, obviously out of focus point sources of light. The fact they are out of focus indicates immediately that they are close to the camera and more than likely within a few metres. As the camera's focus is set to infinity - the earth would be out of focus otherwise - the objects cannot be at any great distance from the lens as most of them show blatant and typical Airy disks. This simple fact precludes them from being large objects at a distance.

The flashing that these things often exhibit, is due to the fact that these objects are tumbling. For me, ice crystals is a very nice explanation and perfectly plausible. We know that the shuttle dumps urine, which would freeze and travel along with the spacecraft as it shares the same initial trajectory and velocity. The crystals glow with reflected sunlight and would appear to flash as they tumble. They would also not show up if they were in shadow and could seem to appear and disappear without warning - just as the lights do in the STS 60(80) footage.

Furthermore, the objects would not all share the same trajectory and would appear to move pretty much at random.

This is exactly what is observed in most of the 'smoking gun' shuttle footage around at the moment. I would further posit that if these objects are not ice crystals, then where are the ice crystals, because they should be visible? No-one else seems to have bothered asking that question!

You can't do a decent analysis of the motion of these objects unless you model their motions in 3D. These objects are not moving 2 dimensionally, but all the analyses I've seen on their motions - such as that done on STS 48 by Jack Kasher has been done in 2D and is fundamentally flawed. He has based his calculations on the assumption that these objects are distant - a pretty big assumption and one that does not stand up to close scrutiny of the actual appearance of the objects. He maintains that light from small objects close to the camera would be smeared out to the point of not registering on the CCD chip of the camera. I beg to differ.

It all depends on how bright the light sources are. If these objects were more than about 20 meters from the shuttle, then sure, the light would be smeared too much to be detectable, but if they were only about 2 or 3 meters or so, then they would be perfectly visible. There are other holes in his analysis, but I won't go into them here. The streaks the objects exhibit are camera artifacts and not properties of the objects themselves.

Mir docking footage:

In the case of the Mir docking footage, from the analysis I've done, some of the objects in question actually appear to be background stars. They do not move in relation to one another and all move as would be expected from the shuttle manuvers. The other objects look like ice crystals or other nearby debris to me. The objects appear very bright because the footage is so contrasty - Mir itself appears to glow, which of course it isn't. They really should have stopped the aperture down or tweaked the contrast a bit to improve the image quality.

A final word on astronauts:

I've only known one astronaut. I used to date him. He was trained as a mission specialist along with Andy Thomas, but didn't get his shuttle ride because he refused to change his citizenship - but that's another story. This guy had a wall full of diplomas, certificates and doctorates (3 PhDs - one in celestial mechanics). He flew F18s, but I still had to show him how to work a telescope and he sometimes had trouble with the VCR. Just because they're astronauts doesn't make them experts in everything.

Bye for now

Claire Williams would become my opponent in a debate that neither of us could win because no one really knows the final answer to this mystery. I think of her as an old school personality that would not recognize a UFO if it were to land on top of her head. She would call it a hallucination and seek psychiatric counseling until she could convince herself it wasn't real. Whenever a doctorate in science has spent a lifetime building a belief system, the idea of having it all crumble is like death. It is so devastating, and who wants to die?

Max Planck, the great quantum physicist once said, "A new scientific truth does not triumph by convincing its opponents and making them see the light, but rather because its opponents eventually die and a new generation grows up that is familiar with it." That is exactly what would happen in a long debate I would have with Clare William, as you will see. I wrote her a long letter attacking her ideas like a maniacal tiger. She replied with the same vengeance. We were at each other's throats in a debate that infuriated me to no end. I could not stand how scientists were so conservative to suggest we were alone in the universe and bend the intent of their thoughts with the cleverness of scientific reason. Clare Williams wrote me the following letter paraphrasing my letter and responding to each statement.

Hello David,

DS: Dear Claire Williams, You can fool an untrained physicists or even a UFO enthusiast but you are not very observant. I suggest you try Zen meditation for ten years and look again at the Tether.

CW: Thank you for your concern for my spiritual well being. I hope to

be able to convince you that I am a reasonably observant person and certainly more observant than you give me credit for being.

DS: I have led a 4-year investigation into all of this footage at NASA and from other sources. The information I have will rock your observatory.

CW: I too have been investigating this stuff for several years and have come to my own conclusions for very good reasons.

DS: But thank God I am talking to a scientist. I will explain your errors one by one on the STS-75 "Tether Incident". I will address each of your points:

1. If you have a good quality copy (any maybe you don't),

CW: The quality of my tape is not too bad. I have performed successful analysis before on worse.

DS: The discs are clearly passing "behind" the tether as the light that reflects off of the tether and ionized nitrogen gas (see NASA report as to why the tether appeared so bright) obscures the light reflecting off of the discs.

CW: The tether appears much brighter than the disks, but this because the light from the disks is being smeared out over the focal plane of the camera's optics. The tether is not obscuring the light from the swarming objects, nor can it. There are some objects moving in the background. These are the stars, but they are at a different focus to the swarming objects and this is the nub of my proof. The swarming objects are in the foreground because if they were at the distance of the tether, they would share the same focus (infinity setting) as the stars and they do not. An object that is reflecting or emitting light has a quantifiable brightness. When you look at that object with any optical system the light will appear most concentrated and the object will appear brightest when all the light being received from it is being focused into the smallest possible area of your focal plane. It makes no difference whether you are talking about a camera, a video camera (tube or CCD) or a telescope.

To illustrate my point, let's consider the case of a magnifying glass and the sun for moment. When you focus the rays of the sun with a magnifying glass you can generate enough heat to start a fire by concentrating all the energy received by the lens into one small spot. If you defocus the sunlight by moving your magnifying glass closer or further away, you spread the energy out over a larger area and it becomes much more difficult to start that fire.

We are dealing with the same principle with the objects in the tether footage. When the focus is shifted to the tether, the objects are defocused and their light becomes smeared out over a wider area of the focal plane of the camera and they appear less bright than they did when they were in focus. There are only a limited number of photons coming from the objects to go around. When the light from any pinpoint light source is focused, all the photons land in pretty much the same spot and the object looks very bright. When the light is smeared out over a wider area on the focal plane, the photons are spread out and fewer land in the same spot so the object appears less bright, although we are receiving the same number of photons in both cases.

The light coming from the objects has the cross section of a cone. When the light passes through a lens, the light rays are refracted and brought to a convergent point (the apex of the light cone), which is its focal point. The rays of light converge at different places for objects at different distances from the lens. If you shift the focus, you move the focal plane through the light cone and your object (actually its Airy disk in this instance) appears to increase or decrease in diameter. This is not to be confused with changing magnification or zooming. I learnt this stuff in high school. Didn't you? Or perhaps, like most people, you weren't paying attention because all this stuff is SO BORING!!!

DS: There are no frayed edges or blurring of the light off the discs as they pass "behind" the tether.

CW: You are making the classic mistake here of thinking that when an object is out of focus, it will appear fuzzy. This is not the case with pinpoint light sources and lenses. Hence my lengthy dissertations on

Airy disks. You don't have to take my word for this. You can prove it for yourself with a very simple experiment. I don't know what equipment you have at your disposal, but you could try a pair of binoculars, a telescope, a camera or preferably a video camera if you have one. Go outside at night and focus your optical device on a bright star. A distant streetlight will do on a cloudy night, but it has to be a reasonable distance away to be a pinpoint. Now focus your device on the light then play around with the focus. Notice how you don't get a fuzzy light, but a nice crisp looking disk instead. This is what I am talking about.

DS: To cause a field reversal on film (to reverse a foreground object with a background object) the background object would have to be as bright as our sun and this effect would cause the edges of the foreground object to have light bleed around the edges. Yet in this video, there is no bleeding of edges. The edges of the discs are crisp. They do not radiate more light than the tether. They therefore could not cause a field reversal effect.

CW: This is totally irrelevant to the needs of our discussion so I'm not even going to go into it (notice how she avoids this paramount discussion).

DS: 2. If these were foreground objects, they would have to be reflecting more light, not less, than the light reflecting off of the tether. They are clearly farther behind the tether than they appear as they reflect very little light

CW: Unknowingly, you have just proven my point. See above. These objects are reflecting sunlight, just as the tether is. They are not being illuminated by the tether. They appear brightest when they look like pinpoints or tiny dots. For your argument to have any validity, these objects would be practically invisible when the focus is shifted to the foreground, just as the stars become harder to see when the focus is shifted away from infinity. Instead, they become brighter when the focus is shifted to the foreground precisely because they are now coming into focus. The light from them is being focused into a smaller area of our detector's surface. The rays of light are converging, just as the rays of light from the stars converge when the focus is shifted to infinity.

DS: 2. If the discs were out-of-focus stars, they would appear to move or Streak in a consistent straight line behind the tether. They do not. These objects are all moving in different directions. Stars cannot do that.

CW: There are stars visible moving in the background and they do all share the same motion. The other objects are in the foreground (I checked the video double time and she is absolutely wrong about this. The objects are all going in different directions. There are no pinpoint objects that pass in a straight uniform line as stars would. I also doubt weather or not a video camera can capture the light from a distant star at all. The exposure is too fast per second to capture the small amounts of starlight – but this needs to be checked).

DS: Also, these objects are all moving at different rates of speed breaking Galileo's law of gravity.

CW: I think you mean Newton. Galileo never heard of gravity. It was a concept that came sometime after his death (I give Galileo the credit for what Newton gained it for – tests on falling bodies all falling at the same rate of speed towards gravity regardless of weight and size and density, for it was Galileo who did the experiments).

DS: If they were natural objects under the influence of gravity, they would all be falling through the void of space in the same direction as gravity pulls and all at the same speed. They do not.

CW: They are moving under the influence of gravity, just not in the way you think. These objects are in freefall. They are in orbit around the Earth, just as the shuttle and tether are, but that does not mean that they share the same trajectories. The objects originated in the shuttle and as such are moving with the same initial velocity and in the same orbit, as the shuttle. However, each of them has been given an additional acceleration, which provided it with its own trajectory. That is why they appear to be moving randomly and yet are still following the shuttle in its orbit. This additional acceleration could have been imparted as the result of the breaking of the tether, particularly if we are talking about small objects, which have been subjected to an electrostatic buildup. The astronauts seemed to think this was debris from the breaking of the tether and they were in a position to know. I see nothing in the footage to contradict this.

DS: 3. If the movement of these so called particles in the foreground (impossible) were under the influence of the shuttles attitude thrusters, they would flare away in the same direction. They do not.

CW: Not necessarily. The particles in the exhaust plume from a jet are not all traveling with in same direction. The material sprays out like water from a hose nozzle (Having seen the video over 100 times, these particles do not behave in any way consistent with "spraying" – again she is blind to this fact).

DS: 4. As to your out-of-focus hog wash, any idiot can put a camera on infinity. All objects farther then 50 feet fall into focus. This can be done manually.

CW: You've proven my point again. Therefore, the objects must by your own admission be closer than 50 feet if they are indeed in focus when I contend...(actually, small pieces of ice or debris blur out so heavily that they barely show any visibility at all on a camera lens when it is focused on infinity – a foreground object has to be very large to remain visible in this instance and Clare or NASA contend "ice crystals or small pieces of debris, which cannot remain visible in the near field of the camera lens when it is focused on infinity).

CW: 5. As to your out-of-focus theory, any object that is out of focus loses so much clarity that all lines blur into each other and cause a consistent fuzzy orb to appear. Background objects, such as trees and buildings, etc do that, but not small light sources. What sort of optics are you using? Extremely poor quality ones I would say if this is your experience. It is certainly not mine. I've been looking at light sources through various optical instruments for over 30 years and for 10 of those years professionally. I didn't get to be head astronomer of a major public observatory because I'm not good at looking at objects through optical instruments. Do you really suppose that I can't tell whether an object is in focus or not? If somebody in my position can't, then who can? A Canadian TV programmer? Please! I've worked for a telescope manufacturer who builds 1 metre-class instruments and satellite laser ranging systems, I've built my own telescope, I've regularly collimated and aligned optical systems. I've helped people grind telescope mirrors and perform optical figuring tests. Before I looked through telescopes for a living, I looked through microscopes. I am in a position to know something about optics and I'm not telling you anything that you can't find in textbooks. What have you done that makes you such an expert? (I have used cameras professionally for over 20 years).

DS: These discs (use your eyes) have obvious portals (squares) cut in the sides of them. These portals make the physics of an out-of-focus theory impossible. If you cannot see these portals clearly, then you have a really bad quality copy of this tape and you must see the real tape.

CW: The 'portals' you refer to are artifacts of the optical system. They are due to an obstruction in the optical path of the camera. Different optical systems can have different obstructions that will appear as different shapes in the Airy disk. I've seen some cameras that show Airy disks that look like half moons, others seem to have little notches cut out of them. Reflecting telescopes can show an Airy disk with a central 'hole' with spikes, due to the obstruction of the secondary mirror and spider. Look carefully at your 'portals'. They all show the same orientation, regardless of the direction of motion of the object (I checked and she is wrong about this fact. In the NASA tape, the square portals have different orientations). Doesn't that seem a little odd to you? If you watch them carefully you can even see the shape change slightly as they drift across the field of view. This is because the camera lens doesn't have a flat field. You can tell a lot about an optical system from Airy disks. This is one of the tricks-of the-trade astronomers learn for collimating telescopes or determining the optical quality of their instruments. You put your instrument on an artificial star (or failing that a real star) and then defocus it to see the shape of the Airy disk. You make your adjustments or carry out your tests while looking at the Airy disk.

DS: 6. You have no idea what NASA has told me as to what these objects are (I am thinking of Dr. Louis A. Frank at NASA who feels the objects are the giant water balls or "small comets" and the others he, an National Space Act Award winning Astrophysicist, feels are "Not easily explained").

CW: If you thought what you had been told was the truth and incontrovertible, you would tell me. I don't know to whom you might have been talking at NASA and neither do I care. If this person was any authority at all, I'm sure he would not mind you mentioning his/her name. There are plenty of people at NASA who would not be qualified to pass an opinion on the matter one way or the other. I've performed my own analysis and come to my own independent conclusions. From the information I have seen from NASA sources on this matter, there is nothing I have to say that they would have any argument with.

DS: You are way off. They do have an explanation that requires true intelligence To debate. If you want to know what that is, I can give you a clue and you Can go from there: a) the video camera on the shuttle is no ordinary camera. I know who makes it. It sees into the Ultraviolet Range, X-ray range and Gamma ray range of light energy spectrum.

CW: I wish! If this were true, then astronomers wouldn't need highly specialized and very expensive instruments to make their observations in different wavelengths (I checked this fact with the Department of Defense and they make such a camera. This fact would be confirmed by Dr. Joe Nuth at NASA). If this camera could pick up these longer wavelengths, then how is it picking up visible light? You obviously know nothing about the EM spectrum or the various wavelengths of radiation within it. The same camera could not possibly be used for visible light, X-rays and gamma rays (not to be confused with cosmic rays) without extensive modifications to the

radiation-gathering end of the apparatus. That is why we needed to create a special space telescope customized for X-ray observations and another for gamma ray observations and yet another for optical observations. It would have been a much cheaper alternative if we could have had all three in the one instrument, but alas, it was not possible. The same detector might be fitted to different devices, which are customized for specific wavelengths, but not for all at once. I can believe that the shuttle camera might see some little way into the UV end of the spectrum, but not very far and it certainly wouldn't extend to the much longer wavelengths of X-rays and gamma rays. Ask your friend again and this time, tell him you know an astronomer who would very much like a demonstration of this wonder camera!

DS: As an astronomer, you may begin to start your observations there. As any object radiating in this spectrum with no residue in the lower energy spectrum must be a high-energy quantum phenomenon.

CW: This might be true if we were indeed seeing objects radiating X-rays and gamma rays, but unfortunately this is not what we are dealing with. Your source has misled you there.

Clare Williams is obviously furious here because there is something going on at NASA that she does not know about and she feels a little embarrassed. I was not misled. I researched the NASA video camera's capabilities through the Department of Defense. What I found was a company called Advanced Photonix in Camarillo, California who makes photo diodes, which is boasts in its press release, "LAAPDs are the first solid state devices to offer sufficient gain, low enough background noise, and adequate active areas to replace photomultiplier tubes in numerous applications. They bring the same qualities of ruggedness, small size, and low cost to low-level light detection that charged-coupled device cameras have brought to video camcorders. LAAPDs are fast detectors of low-light levels. They span the near ultraviolet (invisible to human eyes), visible, and near infrared spectra, and are sensitive to charged particles and ionizing radiation. When coupled with a scintillation counter, they also detect x rays and gamma rays." The press release by Advanced Photonix also stated that the LAAPDs are also "leading to innovations and applications for other agencies as well, such as U.S. Department of Energy, NASA, and the Defense Advanced Research Projects Agency."

Later, Dr. Nuth at NASA confirmed that the video camera on the shuttle was capable of exactly what Advanced Photonix claimed here, when he wrote me on April 3, 2000: "Although the camera itself may respond to x-rays and gamma rays (usually as noise), the optics do not serve to focus on anything but visible and near-UV photons. I would be amazed if the optics were not quartz so that the UV cut-off wavelength would be ~ 180nm. If sapphire the cut-off drops to 160nm and for CaF2 the cut-off is ~ 135nm. In no case can the camera focus either x-rays or gamma rays."

While Clare Williams was proven wrong on this very elaborate point, she does not realize that the Near Ultraviolet light spectrum is exactly where Dr. Louis A. Frank made his discovery of the invading "small comets" allegedly made of water. Dr. Frank also admitted to me that he thought the objects were what we were seeing in the NASA video in part. The fact the objects only showed up in the Near Ultraviolet light spectrum, as previously discussed, suggest that they are very high-energy objects. None of what Dr. Frank had wrote to me about suggested Claire William's "Airy Discs," which, being a top astrophysicist at NASA, one would expect he would if he thought that is what they were. He did not. In fact his silence mystifies me, as I think he knows the real truth.

Let us continue with my debate with Clare Williams:

DS: There is something plain and in your sight that you still can't see: that is that these DISCS are pulsing with very sophisticated wave patterns that repeat themselves in proper sequence over and over. I have studied these wave patterns very carefully. They are beyond anything science has ever seen.

CW: These pulsing you see is due the fact that these are irregularly shaped particles and they're tumbling. As they tumble, they reflect different amounts of light into the camera from their irregular surfaces. The pulsation rate tells you the speed at which the objects are rotating or tumbling.

DS: They show gravity waves stronger than light that bend gravity frequencies of visible light into their shape (gravity beyond light speed wave).

CW: You'd have to run that by me again because that made no sense to me whatsoever. I think you are trying to tell me that gravity waves travel faster than light and that somehow these objects are generating gravity waves to bend light. But that's not how it comes out. (This is exactly what I was trying to show her but she cannot see this yet, as most astrophysicists do not believe that there is a force beyond light speed).

DS: When you see a good (very damned good) quality copy of this mission, you will see what I am talking about. No debris, space junk or star pulses like this. Not what I am seeing.

CW: I don't want to get into a discussion on gravity waves with you, but I can tell from what you've written here, that you don't really understand the concept. I think you are referring to gravity lensing (also called microlensing) - but I don't think that's what we're dealing with here. Tumbling particles is a much more satisfactory explanation for me. We don't have to resort to all this exotic speculation so explain what is recorded on the tape. There is a much simpler, prosaic explanation and one that is consistent with the facts.

The other question your theory would have to answer is why these objects were not visible to observers on the ground. From what you've written here, I know you're going to try to, tell me that these objects were able to cloak themselves using gravity waves. Why then were they visible to the shuttle camera, if they were trying to hide?

If these objects were as large as Martyn Stubbs contends, then they should have been clearly visible to observers on the ground. The shuttle is only a few tens of metres long and it is visible from the ground, much smaller objects are also visible to ground-based observers. An object hundreds of metres in diameter would have been glaringly obvious to observers on the ground. Each one of these objects should have been brighter than Venus in the dawn sky. The fact is that they weren't. Tiny particles such as debris from the tether or ice crystals wouldn't show up from the ground, although
it would be visible to the shuttle camera. Ask yourself which is the simpler and more rational explanation: out of focus debris in the foreground or mile-wide spacecraft with exotic, though not very effective, cloaking devices?

Claire Williams doesn't understand that what we are seeing on the NASA tape may well be only visible in the near Ultra Violet light spectrum, invisible to the human eye. If this is the case, then of course no one on the ground could see the UFOs. In fact, the astronauts could not see them without the aid of the special video camera and filters that allows them to see into the Near UV.

DS: If you want to see still photos taken out of the three phase pulse and my real hard data on this, please contact me and give me your mailing address. I will send you a real tape and the real data. Then we can have an intelligent conversation.

CW: Thank you for the offer, but to be honest, I doubt that anything you have to show me will change my opinion. I don't like to give out my personal mailing address, however, if you insist, the mailing address for the observatory is on our website.

www.cfmeu.asn.au/planetarium.

I would like to thank you for taking the time to write to me as you have provided me with a very useful insight into how a layman interprets what he's seeing in this sort of footage. I guess a case could be made if NASA does turn out to be 'hiding' this footage, that it might well be precisely because it is so highly susceptible to misinterpretation to the untrained eye. I doubt very much that a good case can be made for them hiding it though. It was broadcast on NASA TV after all and that's how Martyn got hold of it in the first place.

Kind regards
Clare

Clare Williams
When we cease to explore, we cease to be human.
Head Astronomer & Planetarium Manager
Canberra Space Dome & Observatory

I expect that the majority of the public would believe an explanation like the one Clare Williams gave to me. That is because fine loop-hole in her explanation go right over the tops of everyone's heads.

When Thomas Edison was searching for a material to use for the filament of the first incandescent lamp, his foreman came to him and said, "Mr. Edison, I am sorry to say we have done a thousand experiments and worked thousands of hours to find this filament and I am afraid to say, it has all been for nothing." Edison replied, "Nonsense, we know a thousand ways in which it doesn't work!" I use this aphorism to show how science progresses by elimination the theories that do not hold up under scientific scrutiny. But it is only under absolute scrutiny that I could debate with Clare Williams, because for the case of a simple argument, she would appear to have won this debate with me, ten to two. But my two would become ten after I found more evidence and amazing phenomenon.

Of course, I have to be open to the possibility that I might be wrong, and all the other data I have presented here is just good science fiction. Clare Williams wrote to me again after I had called her a "liar," the following letter:

Hello David,

CW: Firstly, let me tell you that I do not appreciate being called a liar. There are many people out there who are trying to pull the wool over your eyes, but I am not one of them. In fact, I am trying very hard to clarify some very simple principles for people, so that they have the tools to discern the truth for themselves.

I don't ask anybody to take my word for anything. Didn't I, in fact, ask you to perform some simple experiments to verify my assertions about the focus of the objects for yourself. This is not a difficult thing to do.

Just exactly what do you think it is that I am lying to you about and on what evidence do you base this allegation?

DS: Dear Claire Williams, Thank you for taking the time to write me. No, I am not a layperson.

CW: Would you kindly tell me what it is you do? I can tell that you are not an astronomer or a physicist.

DS: And yes, I do know the electromagnetic spectrum well. I also know Max Planck's $E = hf$ well and regard it higher than Einstein's formula for reasons that Tesla proved.

CW: I personally don't hold any one equation in any higher regard than any other. You can't really divide physics up and say that this bit is more important than that bit. I too am familiar with the work of Tesla and was a founding member of the local Tesla Society. I have an enormous respect for Nicola Tesla. He was a very brilliant man and years ahead of his time, but he wasn't right about everything.

DS: The video camera on the shuttle is a super camera. There are many video cameras that DoD and other agencies retrofit and make for NASA. Their depth of field is phenomenal (making airy disc theories less plausible)

CW: Yes, the camera has a very good focal range. I don't dispute that, but this doesn't mean that every object within its field of view is in focus all the time. It cannot focus on objects that are both distant and nearby at the same time and this is clearly evidenced by the appearance of the objects on the videotape. I am at a loss to know how I can explain this to you in any simpler language than I have already used. You obviously haven't conducted the experiment with the video camera I suggested. If you had, you would have verification for yourself of what of I have been trying to tell you. As well as their ability to detect photons in the visible and near UV range simultaneously. While they do not claim to see into the far and extreme UV range of the electromagnetic spectrum, there are special detectors that make them sensitive to x-rays and gamma rays as "background radiation" I am told.

You are being misinformed or you are not quite understanding what you are being told if you think that these are the capabilities of the shuttle video cameras. X-ray and gamma ray detectors are highly specialized instruments and do not record visible wavelengths. If my suspicions are correct, then this is where you think James Oberg and myself are lying to you - in the camera's capabilities. Am I correct?

DS: I do understand that to have a camera that can see into the full known electromagnetic spectrum (radio-infrared-visible-uv-x-ray-gamma, etc.) would be impossible to do. With the type of cameras NASA is using now and some of their UV explorer satellites and special films made by Kodak, of course they can take pictures into the known electromagnetic spectrum.

CW: Personally I don't know of anybody who is still using film for professional astronomical observations, mostly it is done using electronic detectors these days, photoelectric photometry is the technical term for it. Visible light is only a small part of that spectrum.

DS: Dr. Earl Van Landingham, Now NASA Director of the Office of Space Access & technology, once told me that, "If an extraterrestrial craft were to arrive at Earth from another star system, it would have to be capable of such great speeds, it would radiate with such tremendous energy, we would detect it well in advance."

CW: I would agree with that assessment. If you'd asked me I would have told you pretty much the same thing. That doesn't mean, however, that such a thing has been detected. and I'm willing to lay odds that Dr Landingham hasn't told that such a discovery has been made either.

DS: As the UV range of the electromagnetic spectrum is the high-energy part of the light spectrum, that is where such a signal would be detectable, not necessarily down in the radio frequency range of the EMS. I believe SETI is looking in the wrong part of the spectrum.

CW: SETI isn't looking for the arrival of interstellar spacecraft. It's looking for signals from an extraterrestrial civilization and one that may not even be capable of interstellar space travel yet. Or at least one that wouldn't send out an expedition unless it had a pretty fair expectation of finding something at its destination.

DS: Curiously, NASA's video and other film cameras on the shuttle are looking into the full electromagnetic spectrum, even down in infrared. Most of the new satellites are looking in the Far and Extreme UV range such as ORFEUS SPAS II launched in 1996 on
STS-80.

CW: I regularly receive updates from a variety of such projects. I publish them in a newsletter I produce.

DS: I believe many of the phenomena seen on these missions are high-energy phenomena.

CW: I believe so too. I see many of those 'phenomena' as cosmic rays, but I don't agree that any other high-energy event is being recorded by the shuttle video cameras.

DS: Whether they are space ships or not, I do not know for sure. I do know that I have seen a real flying saucer in Berkeley, California, in 1968 as clear as day. There were over 100 people on the street that

day. No one could tell me that what I saw was a balloon or a flying pizza. I know they are out there.

CW: It may surprise you to learn that I have too have seen things I cannot explain. I have had at least 4 daylight sightings of large anomalous objects. That is why I have spent the best part of the last 30 years investigating and researching UFOs. I'm looking for answers.

CW: Contrary to what some would have you believe, I am not a debunker. Yes, I am skeptical, only a fool wouldn't be. There are an awful lot of people out there who are more interested in sensationalism than the truth. I don't happen to be one of them. I happen to believe that people do see anomalous things and that there is a genuine mystery at the heart of many UFO sightings, but I don't believe there is any evidence for it on those Shuttle videotapes.

Bye for now

Clare

Dear Clare Williams,

I wanted to ask you if I could have permission to use the letters you wrote to me for my book, "The Case For NASA UFOs?" I will use them verbatim as I am looking for a critic of this footage who disagrees with the UFO theory.

CW: If you want something to put in your book, I would be happy to prepare something more suitable for you - a proper statement, rather than just snippets from email.

P.S. I have studied hours of this footage and do see what are genuine airy discs and they are so fuzzy, and none of them have notches in them and none of them pulse. The ones with the notches are the really, really out of focus ones, I'm afraid. I did start writing a paper on this whole thing, but my partner has convinced me that there's really no point in carrying on with it as UFO Mag have already made a mockery of the whole thing and he thinks I'm wasting my time. I've considered his wishes and have agreed as we already have too many other things going on in our lives at the moment for me to give this my full attention anyway. In any case, I figure I've almost said everything I wanted to say on the matter now and just formalizing those ideas probably won't contribute much more. I have actually asked Graham Birdsall for an apology for publishing my comments to him - which I foolishly believed were going no further - on his website as he never sought my permission to take part in his 'debate'. Had he asked I would never have agreed as I don't believe it was an appropriate forum. As I said to him, if he'd asked me for something he could publish, I would have prepared a proper paper for him rather than the quick off-the-cuff comments he got.

Thank you at least for doing me the courtesy of asking. As a professional writer myself, the only things I like to see published are things I have written and duly authorized for publication. This saves everyone the embarrassment of publishing comments that might be misconstrued or published out of context. I still stand by the points I made below, but I would like an opportunity to polish it up for you and perhaps even add some new information.

Good Luck with your book

Clare

I wrote Joe Nuth at NASA sending him a copy of my first letter to Clare Williams. I wanted his opinion on the matter after the disaster of Martyn Stubbs sharing my letters from NASA with UFO Magazine in England. I was so embarrassed and I knew this was the end of the openness of my dialogs with Joe Nuth. Of course NASA would share nothing with me now, as his name was in the center of the

UFO propaganda tossed into the UFO community. UFO magazine even wrote Dr. Nuth on their own behalf to try and get some answers of their own as they could not legally publish my letters without my permission. I did not give them my permission.

The following is a letter I received from Dr. Joe Nuth on April 3, 2000 via e-mail:

Dear Mr. Sereda,

My replies will be put below your comments: I've underlined them so that they will be easier for you to find.

Joe Nuth

DS: Dear Dr. Nuth, I must appologize for your name being involved by these idiots in England with regards to UFO magazine. I did not give them your letters. The man who is my source to NASA shuttle videotapes, Martyn Stubbs, did that. I realize they have distorted our conversations. I am writing a book about this that will be published. For the record, I transcribe your e-mails to me in full, as well as those from other sources at NASA.

JN: No problem with this. I'm not sure that such "recognition" goes beyond the readers of the magazine.

DS: As to STS-75 and the "Tether Incident," I sent the following letter to the head of an observatory, Claire Williams, in Australia:

Dear Claire Williams,

DS: 1. If you have a good quality copy (any maybe you don't), the discs are clearly passing "behind" the tether as the light that reflects off of the tether and ionized nitrogen gas (see NASA report as to why the tether appeared so bright) obscures the light reflecting off of the discs. There are no frayed edges or blurring of the light off the discs as they pass "behind" the tether. To cause a field reversal on film (to reverse a foreground object with a background object) the background object would have to be as bright as our sun and this effect would cause the edges of the foreground object to have light bleed around the edges. Yet in this video, there is no bleeding of edges. The edges of the discs are crisp. They do not radiate more light than the tether. They therefore could not cause a field reversal effect.

DS: 2. If these were foreground objects, they would have to be reflecting more light, not less, than the light reflecting off of the tether. They are clearly farther behind the tether than they appear as they reflect very little light.

JN: Again, I suggest that there is the possibility that these objects are very close to the Shuttle Bay camera and therefore may not be as bright as hypothesized. This is consistent with your descriptions of their motions as discussed below in that they are influenced by very subtle conditions in the cargo bay while essentially co-orbiting with the Shuttle.

DS: 2. If the discs were out-of-focus stars, they would appear to move or streak in a consistent straight line behind the tether. They do not. These objects are all moving in different directions. Stars cannot do that. Also, these objects are all moving at different rates of speed breaking Galileo's law of gravity. If they were natural objects under the influence of gravity, they would all be falling through the void of space in the same direction as gravity pulls and all at the same speed. They do not. Satellites also revolve around the Earth is straight lines and in orbits that are consistent with the motion of gravity all in the same direction.

DS: 3. If the movement of these so called particles in the foreground (impossible) were under the influence of the shuttles attitude thrusters, they would flare away in the same direction. They do not.

JN: The above conjecture depends on when and where the particles were released. The thruster firings could easily shake loose additional batches of debris.

DS: 4. As to your out-of-focus hog wash, any idiot can put a camera on infinity. All objects farther then 50 feet fall into focus. This can be done manually.

DS: 5. As to your out-of-focus theory, any object that is out of focus looses so much clarity that all lines blur into each other and cause a consistent fuzzy orb to appear. These discs (use your eyes) have obvious portals (squares) cut in the sides of them. These portals make the physics of an out-of-focus theory impossible. If you cannot see these portals clearly, then you have a really bad quality copy of this tape and you must see the real tape.

6. You have no idea what NASA has told me as to what these objects are. You are way off. They do have an explanation that requires true intelligence to debate. If you want to know what that is, I can give you a clue and you can go from there:

a) the video camera on the shuttle is no ordinary camera. I know who makes it. It sees into the Ultraviolet Range, X-ray range and Gamma ray range of light energy spectrum. As an astronomer, you may begin to start your observations there. As any object radiating in this spectrum with no residue in the lower energy spectrum must be a high-energy quantum phenomenon.

JN: Although the camera itself may respond to x-rays and gamma-rays (usually as noise), the optics do not serve to focus anything but visible and near-UV photons. I would be amazed if the optics were not quartz so that the UV cut- off wavelength would be ~180nm. If saphire the cut-off drops to 160nm and for CaF2 the cut-off is ~135nm. In no case can the camera focus either x-rays or gamma-rays.

7. There is something plain and in your sight that you still can't see: that is that these DISCS are pulsing with very sophisticated wave patterns that repeat themselves in proper sequence over and over. I have studied these wave patterns very carefully. They are beyond anything science has ever seen. They show gravity waves stronger than light that bend gravity frequencies of visible light into their shape (gravity beyond light speed wave). When you see a good (very damned good) quality copy of this mission, you will see what I am talking about. No debris, space junk or star pulses like this. Not what I am seeing.

If you want to see still photos taken out of the three-phase pulse and my real hard data on this, please contact me and give me your mailing address. I will send you a real tape and the real data. Then we can have an intelligent conversation.

JN: I do know of Dr. Chang-Diaz and will try to call him concerning these observations in the near future. I will be especially interested to learn if he observed such objects from the Shuttle windows or just on the bay cameras.

DS: Dr. Nuth, Dr. Franklin Chang-Diaz is the physicist that was on that mission and saw this. He commented live on the video broadcast. Dr. Franklin Chang-Diaz's phone number is (281) 283-5535 in Houston. He is Director of the NASA Advanced Space Propulsion Lab at the Johnson Space Center. He knows what he saw in the UV range on camera that day. Perhaps you can ask him. I sent him the tape also.

I never did hear back from Dr. Nuth about his dialog with Dr. Franklin Chang-Diaz. Perhaps Franklin didn't tell him anything. I do not know. Perhaps he did tell him and it is classified.

At this point, the debate looked weak on my side of the fence from a political perspective. I could not get NASA to come out and candidly admit to a phenomenon of gargantuan proportions, such as I was suggesting. I didn't feel a loss though. I really felt that the agency and its advocacies were being very deceptive. There were too many loopholes in their theories. The real evidence I presented in earlier chapters revealed an amazing phenomena taking place out in space. I was not surprised that NASA wanted it all covered up. But what if I was wrong and all of this was a coincidence?

"When senior scientists say something can be done, they are usually right. When they something cannot be done, they are often wrong." - R. W. Hamming (paraphrase by BJM).

I was going to attempt to put myself in the position against all public perception of what NASA was shoving down on the top of the minds of all inquiring Americans. Only a fool would put one's self in such a position, because if I am wrong, and dearly proven wrong, who would believe me when I said I found yet another mystery? No one. R.W. Hamming's words would act as my mentor as I tried to get an icon in the UFO world to agree with me. I had made a good contact to a young wealthy man named Joe Firmage, who was a self-made billionaire turned UFO advocate. I sent him the NASA footage and some of my data and he wrote me back the following letter via e-mail:.

Dear Mr. Sereda,

I agree that if the lights can be demonstrated to fall behind the tether miles distant, then they are not debris. It seemed that the nature of the video sensitivity was such that dim objects might appear to be behind, but out of focus near objects would appear as large and dim and fast moving, in all directions.

Three things on your analysis. I don't understand all of the points you are trying to make RE gravity, and would like to talk through it at some point. Second, based upon Joe Nuth's comments, I don't believe he is lying or covering up anything. Third, if there are demonstrable accelerations of some and not all objects, or geometric patterns in the positions of the lights, or if distance can be proven, you have something very important. I would like nothing more than for you to be right, but I'm still very much undecided based upon a first review of I can see on the tape. It would be helpful to have pointed out the specific lights to watch most carefully.

Stay well – Joe Firmage

Joe Firmage reviewed the tape more seriously in the following months. I thought he was a strong advocate of revealing government conspiracies and cover-ups. Firmage later took sides with NASA in this debate. He did not believe anything of significance was happening on these videos. I was hoping he would fund deeper research, but it was over with him at the start.

When I researched Firmage and the International Space Science Organization he founded, I learned that he had employed many ex-NASA scientists. NASA was all over Firmage's organization. Of course the answer was staring me right in the face. Why would Firmage and his organization have an opinion about this footage, which is contrary to what NASA had already publicly stated. But why would Joe Firmage, an alleged UFO advocate, found a science organization to research UFOs? Was he being implanted by the CIA to merely pretend? Were there deeper reasons that NASA had in mind for Joe Firmage, reasons that required a UFO enthusiast to collect information from UFO researchers? At this point, I didn't trust Joe Firmage. I felt that he too either sold out to the agency or he was always with them.

I recall the TV show "The X-Files" aphorism "Trust no one." Now I couldn't trust anyone. I knew there was something deeper going on at NASA after I weighed all the evidence and all of the communications. Where would I go next? Would there be a deeper answer or was this the end of my research into this project?

Chapter Eight
The Ancient Future

"It is dangerous to be right when the government is wrong" - Voltaire

I – The Dropa Stone Connection

In April of 2000, I was being filmed and interviewed for a TV special in Hollywood for Twentieth Century Fox on UFOs. It was called, "UFOs, The Best Evidence Caught on Tape II" produced by Robert Kiviat. It aired on Fox TV on April 27th. One of his researchers, David Ballard, also a producer, brought forward some amazing evidence from a distant source source. The answer came from ancient China.

In 1938, a Chinese and Tibetan team of archaeologists led by Chinese professor Chi Pu Tei from the University of Beijing, discovered an astounding burial site high in the mountains of BayanKara-Ula on the border of Tibet and China. The team of archaeologists were conducting a detailed survey of a series of interlocking caves. What they found would provide evidence for this investigation to suggest the impossible. We would be able to clearly hypothesize where these NASA UFOs came from. But the answer would shock the world.

The Chinese and Tibetan team found a gravesite containing the skeletal remains of what at first were thought to be a very primitive and tiny people with extra-large heads. Professor Chi Pu Tei is reported to have responded, "Who ever heard of apes burying one another?" Of course they were not apes.

It was all too familiar to the descriptions Ufologists give to the Grays: the small aliens with the little bodies and the big heads. The team found that the cave area is still inhabited by two tribes that have some of the same physical characteristics. They are frail in their bodies and stand between 3-foot-6 and 4-foot-7 with an average body height of 4-foot-2. The two tribes are known today as the Hans and the Dropas. These are the same sizes that eye-witness accounts give to the Grays.

Then the team found a large round stone disc half buried in the dirt on the floor of one of the caves. The discs were a record of some ancient event or an artifact of something these ancient peoples described seeing some 12,000 years ago. Most captivating to my eyes was the remarkable perfect match that these ancient artifacts provided when compared with the UFOs captured on the 1996, NASA STS-75 space shuttle mission.

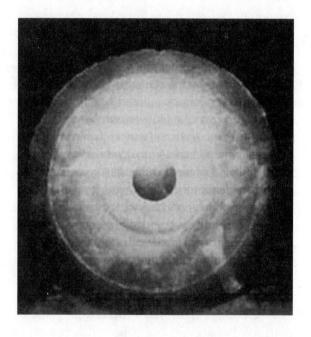

Photo of Dropa Stone Disc

This photograph of an ancient Dropa stone shows a round disc, a hole in the center and a rectangular notch carved out of the side (which has now been filled in) visible on the lower right of the photograph. The fact that the rectangular notch has been filled in suggests that the archaeologists must have thought that the notches were damaged, but maybe they were mistaken. The Dropa stone disc also has a fine spiraling groove radiating out from the center to the rim, which is described by the archaeologists but not clearly visible in this photo.

The groove contains ancient closely written characters in a language that would later be translated by another Chinese scientist named Dr. Tsum um Nui in 1962. In 1965, 716 more grooved Dropa stone discs were discovered in the same caves.

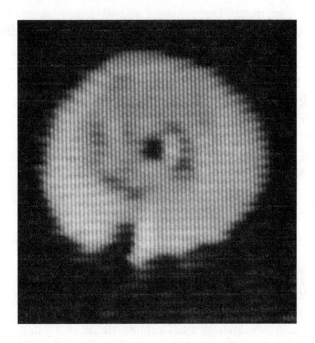

NASA STS-75 "Tether Incident" UFO

When we compare this amazing NASA UFO photo to the Dropa Stone discs, we see a perfect match. We see a disc-shaped craft, the black hole in the center, the rectangular notch out of the side and a spiraling wave radiating out from the center of the circle to the rim, all identical to the 12,000 year old Dropa Stones. Could this be the very "signature" that these extraterrestrial visitors wanted us to see? The fact that the spiraling gravity wave was only visible for a fraction of a second inside of a three-phase pulse is even more disturbing.

I pondered the odds of an event like this happening in space in the year 1996, and an event some 12,000 years ago in ancient China and then finding a perfect match. It was too astounding for me to comprehend. I couldn't assume numbers but the odds would have to be greater than a million to one to get a match like this. This couldn't just be a coincidence, I thought.

Could these ancient peoples of China and Tibet have recorded an event 12,000 years ago describing UFOs right down to a magnetic pulsing wave of energy? I felt that the evidence was so compelling, I wanted to learn more. There may be an answer here that could tell us just who or what is visiting Earth today and most importantly, where are our modern-day visitors from?

Chinese professor Dr. Tsum Um Nui, started to try and decode the characters carved inside of the fine spiraling grooves of the Dropa Stones in 1962. When he broke the code of this ancient language, probably written by the neighboring tribes who actually saw and described the story that would unfold, he was banned by the Beijing University Prehistory Department from publishing his findings. Eventually, the story he found was published. The story would challenge everything modern scientists believe about our human origins.

Dr. Tsum Um Nui's banned discovery told of a story 12,000 years old or more. He said it is written on these discs that:

A spacecraft of some kind from another planet had crash-landed. A dark gray overcast sky beckoned the ancient Chinese peoples on a late autumn afternoon. A deep rumbling sound shook the ground, sending animals fleeing and startling birds from their nests. The people had never heard thunder quite like this. A small group of hunters stalking deer cast their eyes to the sky, expecting the clouds to break open from the deafening thunder with rain. Instead, a glowing ball of light streaked across the sky above their heads. The disc shaped object fell from the sky and crash-landed to the ground. It landed walking distance away from the hunters. They were afraid.

When the hunters found the crashed disc-shaped object, they described it as shiny with a hole in the side of it (the square notches) and then they saw something moving inside. This was probably one of the aliens. The story reveals that the Dropa Stone discs are an ancient artifact that best describes what the crash-landed spacecraft looked like. But how astounding. They match perfectly with the UFOs videotaped on the NASA Space Shuttle missions in 1996 (STS-75). Where would all this lead?

Legend still preserved in the area spoke of a small race of people who came from the clouds long, long ago in ancient times. The men have huge bulbous heads and tiny bodies. They were so ugly, that out of fear, the Han tribe killed most of the aliens. The year was approximately 10,000 B.C. Mysteriously, the skeletal remains of the alien bodies in the caves resembled the surviving tribes peoples.

Also, what Professor Chi Pu Tei discovered on the walls of the caves were crude pictographs of the rising Sun, the Moon, unidentifiable stars and the Earth all joined together by lines of pea sized dots. Could these dots have been telling the connection of where the aliens had traveled from?

What the ancient peoples of China saw must have been recorded in stone because, as archaeology has revealed to us, that is how ancient peoples recorded historical events. While the story tells of a crashed spacecraft and aliens, the next clue would be to discover if the translations told of where the aliens said they were from. If we could find that fact, we could clearly hypothesize that the modern-day NASA UFOs are from the same place of origin. One answer may come from studying the pea-sized dots connecting Earth with distant stars. But there were other sources that were more clearly defined.

The implications of being able to match a modern day UFO event with an ancient source would be so ground-breaking for UFO enthusiasts, and even more intimidating for our governments, I could now see why, if this was the truth that NASA had discovered, there would be a cover-up. No one in the public would be allowed to have this knowledge. It would become NASA's biggest secret, assuming NASA researchers found the same truth our research team did. If we could find out through this ancient source where these ancient astronauts are from, then we could easily assume, because of the perfect match, where our modern day visitors are from also.

In 1947, after viewing a Dropa Stone disc, English scientist Dr. Karyl Robin-Evans headed on a journey to the land of the ancient Dzopas traveling through Lhasa (Tibet) where he was granted an audience with the 14th Dalai Lama. On his journey to the land of the Dzopas, he was abandoned by his team because of their natural fear of the terrifying legends of the Baian-Kara-Ula mountain peoples. After a strenuous journey, he made it to the destination.

Dr. Robin-Evans learned the Dzopa dialect from a local language teacher. He later learned from Lurgan-La, the religious guardian of the Dzopa people, the history of the Dzopa people's origins. He was told by the Dzopa that they originally came from a planet in the star system of Sirius about 20,000 years ago. Now our answer has arrived. I had to repeat that in my mind over and over, "Sirius – Ancient Egypt Spoke of Sirius – Sirius, the ancient Egyptian Goddess Isis was said to be from Sirius." The Dzopas told Dr. Robin-Evans that on an exploratory mission in the year 1014, their spacecraft had crash-landed on Earth. This disabled the beings from returning to their home planet in the Star system of Sirius. They had to settle here.

The amazing facts presented by this ancient archeology find tell us that Earth is now inhabited by beings from another star system, more precisely, from the star system Sirius. And we also could assume, if all is correct, that the Sirians have returned. Also, the fact that the Dzopas told Dr. Robin-Evans that there is a periodicity to their Sirian ancestors visits to Earth. From different sources, we have 10,000 B.C. (Dr. Tsum Um Nui), to 18,000 B.C. to the year 1014 A.D. Considering the periodicity to the Sirian visits to Earth, could NASA astronauts have been visited by the same beings back in 1996? The similarities are too astounding to ignore and they will get even more so as we move deeper into the connection to the star Sirius while it shines 8.7 light years away from Earth.

II – One Step Behind NASA

Richard Hoagland, former science advisor to the press wrote in his research that on May 27, 1999, the NASA STS-96 launched at 6:50 A.M. EDT. Not only was Sirius at 33.33 (symbolic of Freemasonry's highest level of enlightenment) above the launch site, but the fact was it was "Sirius," the celestial counterpart to the Egyptian Goddess Isis, rather than Orion or another significant body in the pantheon of NASA deities.

Also, I discovered that this was 3 years after the "Tether Incident" on STS-75, that NASA was launching STS-96 with Sirius at 33.33 degrees from the horizon. That is 3 years later and 33.33 degrees.

It should be noted that all of the "Founding Fathers" of the Constitution of The United States of America were highest degree masons. The Washington monuments were designed with precise Masonic mathematics and alignments.

Could high-ranking officials at NASA also be Highest Degree Masons who wanted to send a message back to the star systems of Sirius saying that "Yes, we understand your message and that you have returned?"

Another amazing fact was that the STS-75 NASA space shuttle was directly over Northern Africa when the swarm of giant UFOs followed in pursuit of making contact. Northern African is of course the home of ancient Egypt and the Pyramids. Was it merely a coincidence or were the Sirian UFOs making contact above the civilization they co-created thousands of years ago?

I couldn't help but think that NASA knew what our research team had finally discovered and more. The question to me was, did NASA follow the same tracks I did and deduct the same hypothesis: that because the UFOs on the 1996, STS-75 "Tether Incident" were identical to the Dropa stones, and that the Dropas told Dr. Robin-Evans that they were from the star system Sirius. Or, did NASA have a deeper source of information, perhaps even direct contact with the Sirians themselves?

The fact that NASA was launching this new mission while Sirius was at 33.33 degrees above the launch window suggests that NASA may be trying to communicate something to the Sirians, perhaps that NASA has received their message loud and clear and NASA was sending a clear message back to them, "We understand where you are from."

But what else do we know about the star system Sirius? What did the ancient Egyptians tell us of this Star system? The Egyptian hieroglyphic symbol for the star Sirius is the triangular face of the pyramid itself. Perhaps this is a sign as to who built the pyramids or who the pyramids were built in honor of: the Sirians. The Goddess Isis is symbolized in ancient Egyptology as being from the star Sirius. In the Great Pyramid, the southern shaft of the Queen's chamber points directly at the star system Sirius at specific times of the year. Facts like these are well known. But there are other facts that are not well known about NASA's latest discoveries and Sirius. These discoveries may help explain to us why NASA is so fascinated with this star system.

In 1976, Royal Archeological Fellow Robert Temple released his book, "The Sirius Mystery." In his work, Temple gives evidence of an ancient African tribe called the Dogon who told of their ancestors coming from the star system Sirius.

Modern astronomers had only identified one star in the Sirius system at the time of the publication of Temple's book. The Sirians told the Dogon of two additional stars in the Sirius system, at the time of his publication, unknown to NASA. It tells a story of Sirius having a main "A" star and a "B" and "C" star that revolve around. The "B" and "C" star revolve in an elliptical orbit around the "A" star every fifty years, say the Dogon priests.

The question was, if this were just a myth lying in no basis of reality, the Dogon tribe would be wrong about their assumptions that there was another star in the Sirius constellation, invisible to astronomers when Temple's book was published and for years following.

In greater detail, the Dogon tribe resides in North West Africa, which is precisely where the space shuttle was during the STS-75 mission "Tether UFO incident" in 1996. The fact that the space shuttle was flying over Northern Africa during the auspicious UFO encounter was even more mystifying to my research when considering the Egyptian and Dogon connection to Sirius. It was all just another signature in the same investigation that pointed to Sirius. The Dogon prophesied that the Sirians (Nommos) "will return." And what better place to return that right over the skies of where the Dogon tribe reside? Was this just another coincidence that astronomers like Clare Williams would disregard?

NASA's scholars attacked Robert Temple for his affiliation with the Dogon tribe's Sirius mystery. He was even blacklisted from numerous jobs after the publication of his book, as he was a former respected member of the world academia. He suffered a great loss in his quest for the truth. He was ostracized from the conservative upper circles of astronomical societies. Of course the conservatives like Clare Williams and others would be upset. They want us all to believe that we are the only ones in the universe and that Contact would happen to them first and the public would be notified of that fact at a later date when the conservatives thought we might be ready to handle it.

At the time of the publication of Temple's book, "The Sirius Mystery," the Dogon tribal tradition insisted that there was a third star in the star system of Sirius. If proven, this star would be called Sirius C. Because this fact could not be proven, Temple was thrown out of respected academia circles and made popular in New Age circles only.

Many years after Temple's book was released, in 1995, the Dogon tribe in Africa and Robert Temple's research would receive a resurrection when French astronomers Daniel Benest and J. L. Duvent published results from their several years of study in the journal of Astronomy and Astrophysics stating that a small red dwarf star, Sirius C, seems to exist in the star system of Sirius. They had detected a perturbation, which cannot be explained by any other theory. The Dogon were correct and modern astronomy was catching up with ancient knowledge.

Temple details in his book, "The Sirius Mystery," how modern astronomers have concurred with the ancient knowledge of the Dogon, finally. Astronomers have now calculated the orbits of the Sirius "B" and "C" stars around Sirius "A" and the Dogon's math was perfect. Modern astronomers calculated their orbits at fifty years, precisely as the Dogon priests had tried to tell us long ago. The Dogon also called Sirius "C" a "heavy" star. What did this mean? What is a heavy star to an ancient peoples? Modern astronomers calculate a star's density by its gravitational pull on surrounding mass or stars. Indeed, they found, Sirius "C" is a "heavy" or dense star just as the ancient Dropa priests had told.

Also, if the Sirius connection were really accurate, there would have to be a planet in the Sirius system for the Sirians to live on. This is also confirmed by Daniel Benest's research in the following abstract published in the journal of Astronomy and Astrophysics on the 12th of December, 1997:

Large stable planetary orbits, already known to exist (more precisely known to be possible from a dynamic point of view), through a systematic exploration of the circular model and for and for several cases of the elliptic model (Sun-Jupiter, Alpha Centauri, Sirius and Coronae Borealis) are found to exist around ADS 12033 A and ADS 12033 B up to distances from each star of the order of more than half the binary's periastron separation. Moreover, nearly circular, stable planetary orbits are found to exist in the so-called "habitable zone" around each star.

Now we have scientific proof of that the Dogon tribe in Africa was correct about there being an additional star is Sirius unknown until 1995, and that the stars in Sirius have "stable planetary orbits," (discovered in 1997), which means life is possible there, we may be able to rely on the Dogons other information . Is science one step behind ancient wisdom. Is the past our very own future?

If the ancients were correct, and it seems that they already proved modern astronomers wrong (while modern astronomers also proved them to be correct), could we assume that the ancients knowledge of the Sirians might also be true?

The African Dogon tribe and the Egyptians told of their own Earthbound civilizations stemming from the star system Sirius. The Summerian-Babylonians, (the most ancient the three), the Egyptians and the African Dogons believed that the Sirians were amphibious by nature: they lived in water and needed it around them to survive. Temple details in his book how the majority of all ancient religions on Earth tell of creator Gods and Goddesses coming to Earth from Sirius, and how these Gods and Goddesses were amphibious by nature. Even the ancient Chinese, in the Han Dynasty (first century AD) tell of five amphibious founders of the Chinese civilization. Two of the fish tailed founders were named Fuxi and Cang Jing.

Robert Temple also documents how the majority of ancient religions on Earth, including Sumerian, Babylonian, Egyptian and Greeks, held the architecture in their sacred rituals of the Sirius "A" star with the Sirius "B" and "C" stars revolving around it every fifty years. Even the Zoastrian religion of ancient Iran (predated Islam) used this sacred geometry in its rituals as a way of invoking the creators from Sirius. The significance of this fact to ancient sources puts a lot of emphasis on creators of human civilization coming from the Sirius star system. If we have proven or even have a good case for the assumption of their return, the news would cause great alarm and excitement to those who understand the significance.

The African Dogon tribes prophesied the return of the Sirians by stating to researchers "The Nommos (Sirians) return will be called the day of the fish" as the Sirians are commonly known as aquatic beings, half fish and half human. The Babylonian God of human creation is called "Oannes," who, in Egyptian, Babylonian, Assyrian, and other cultures is portrayed as a half fish and half human God.

III – Ancient Water – The Signature to NASA's Water Problem

The fact that these ancient sources all pointed to the Sirian creator Gods and Goddesses as amphibious, awoke an astonishing idea in my mind. But the details had to unfold and Robert Temple's book, "The Sirius Mystery," was the best resource. I highly recommend reading it as an addendum to this book, even if it means reading it a second time.

In Robert Temples, book, "The Sirius Mystery," we learn of the Sirian water connection:

> There is some very intriguing evidence for substantial quantities of water on the Giza (Egypt) plateau to be found in the book, "The History of Herodotus, the Greek "Father of History" who lived in the fifth century B.C. and spent a long time in Egypt, of which he left a substantial account which survives today. In his book II, Herodotus discusses the pyramids at some length but does not mention the Sphinx at all. It is therefore practically a certainty that the Sphinx was buried in sand at the time of his

visit. This is an important point to remember. Herodotus strangely states that he was told the following by his Egyptian informants:

They worked in gangs of hundreds thousand men, each gang for three months. For then years the people were afflicted in making the road whereon the stones were dragged, the making of which road was to my thinking a task but a little lighter than the building of the Great Pyramid. For the road is five furlongs long and ten fathoms broad, and raised at its highest to a height of eight fathoms, and it is all of stone polished and carved figures. The ten years aforesaid went to the making of this road and of the underground chambers on the hill whereon the pyramids stand (i.e. the Giza Plateau); these the king meant to be burial-places for himself, and encompassed them with water, bringing in a channel from the Nile.

These translations have largely been ignored by modern Egyptologists. Before we summarize the implications of the water connection to the Sirians, let us read three more passages from Herodotus:

Chephren also built a pyramid, of a less size than his brother's (Cheops was his elder brother). I have myself measured it. It has no underground chambers (we now know this to be false), nor is it entered like the other (the Great Pyramid) by a canal from the Nile, but the river come in through a built passage and encircles an island, in which, they saw Cheops, himself lies.

This point that Cheops himself lies in a manmade island surrounded by water is interesting but it gets better:

Thus far I have recorded what the Egyptians themselves say. Now… I will add thereto something of what I myself have seen. The Egyptians made a labyrinth, a little way beyond the Lake Moeris and near the place called the City of the Crocodiles. I have myself seen it, and indeed no words can tell its wonder: where all that the Greeks have built and wrought added together the whole would be seen to be a matter of less labor and cost than was this labyrinth, albeit the temples of Ephesus and Samos are noteworthy buildings. Though the pyramids were greater than words can tell, and each one of them a match for many great monuments built by Greeks, this maze surpasses even the pyramids.

The text goes on to describe how great amounts of water was channeled into these islands and monuments from the Nile. If the Sirians are actually amphibians as the Egyptians and the African Dogons agreed, certainly a huge artificial lake would be a good place to house the extraterrestrial guests (gods-goddesses). But could the Sirians have requested that the lakes be constructed for their arrival? And what about the Sphinx?

The next thing to note is that the burial-places on the Giza Plateau, or at least one of them, were "encompassed with water." The word "encompassed" indicates that somewhere on the Giza Plateau an important site was surrounded by water. This would have to be the Sphinx, because, as Robert Temple indicates in his research, the Sphinx has signs of erosion around its base, archaeologists believe, to be caused by water. This theory postulates that the Sphinx was surrounded by a moat of water, perhaps to emulate the gods of Sirius having had to be treated the same way upon their arrival and visit to Egypt.

The Sphinx bears the face of the Pharoah, and if encircled by water in the retaining pit, the Pharoah lies there, just as the Egyptians said, in an island surrounded by water. Herodotus said, it was Cheops who lies in the island surrounded by water. Robert Temple writes in his book:

> If we disentangle all of these secondhand accounts recorded by Herodotus, we have a clear tradition in the fifth century BC in Egypt that somewhere on the Giza Plateau (a place where the body of the Sphinx could not be seen) there was at the time of cheops and Kephren an island surrounded by water in which the Pharaoh lay. Since the body of the Sphinx would be covered by water and only the head of the Pharaoh would protrude from the water at that time, it was literally correct to say this. The Pharaoh did indeed lie on an island surrounded by water, if the retaining pit of the Sphinx was full of water, which we

suggest that it was. If it were not, then where is the island on the Giza Plateau? Does anybody know of another candidate?

My suggestion is, therefore, that the Sphinx was surrounded by water originally, and for a significant portion of its history. And furthermore, the record of this fact has been sitting there in the text of Herodotus unrecognized for 2,500 years. As for how the water got there, the raising of the water by simple wooden devices called norias is very ancient and survives today throughout the Nile Delta. I suggest therefore that from the Nile, from the well in the Sphinx Temple or Valley Temple, or by the stone water-conduits excavated on the Giza Plateau in 1995 and 1996, for much of its history the pit around the Sphinx was a moat, and that the Sphinx was kept artificially surrounded by water. Apparently there is still some water beneath the Sphinx today, a fact which has puzzled modern archaeologists.

Robert Temple's compilation of ancient wisdom shows us an astounding new principle: that the Sirians (The Gods and Goddesses of ancient Egypt) were amphibious by nature and had to be kept in, as if, fish tanks or lakes to survive while maintaining contact with the human civilizations. Could the mythological ideas of "mermaids" actually have been Sirian Goddesses? Are we just now beginning to understand the meaning of these ancient myths? I saw, in my research, the most astonishing hypothesis starting to develop.

Robert Temple had a major piece of evidence in the very scientific research I was conducting at NASA. Temple states in his book that, "I believe that the visitation to our planet came from the system of the star Sirius, as the ancient peoples as well as the Dogon have tried to tell us. And since the accounts are of aquatic beings from a watery planet there, it may well be that the reason why the Sphinx – which I believe to have been a statue of Anubus – was sitting in water, was because the visitors from the planet in the system of the star Sirius were amphibious."

Now, if we assume that amphibians have to travel from Sirius, 8.7 light years away from Earth, they would need water to encapsulate their bodies in while they were in transit. Now the hypothesis is starting to reveal itself. Temple writes in his book:

We should not forget that if aquatic amphibious beings are making an interstellar voyage they will need fresh water in their ship in considerable quantities. In the ancient legends of the Sumerians and Babylonians about the god Enki (Ea), who was the god who warned mankind about the Deluge (flood) so that the Ark could be constructed, Enki was said to sleep in a freshwater receptacle or chamber shaped like an Ark, called the Abzu. Could this be a reference to an amphibian in suspended animation? There is at least one occasion in Sumerian literature (fourth to third millennium BC) where the god Enki is described as behaving like an amphibian: "Enki, in the swampland, in the swampland, lies stretched out.."

Temple hypothesizes a connection in this Sumerian tale to what the Dogons said about the Sirians, that they were kept alive in water while they were in the presence of the humans. Temple also tells us that the Dogon "differentiate very clearly between the fiery, roaring landing craft which they describe as bringing the Nommos to Earth, and the new star which appeared in the sky while they were here which would seem to be a reference to their larger base parked in orbit."

So now that we understand in this investigation that the UFOs seen on the NASA, 1996 STS-75 "Tether Incident" are identical in design to the ancient Dropa stones, and that the Dzopas told that they came from the star system of Sirius, and that the Dogon tribe and the Summerian and Babylonian tales concur that the Sirians are amphibious by nature (even Egyptology shows this) then we have to make the assumption that we should be checking our skies and oceans for signs of intelligent watery-like craft and water-based beings.

That fact has been scientifically verified by Dr. Louis A. Frank at NASA. Dr. Louis A. Frank is seeing photographic evidence of 40-ton balls of water, the size of small houses, entering Earth's atmosphere at 35,000 miles per hour, at a rate of over 10 million per year. If Dr. Frank's water balls were intelligent (as if to be amphibious Sirians in transit), rather than randomly hitting Earth like raindrops, they should show signs of intelligence, and remarkably they do.

First of all, as I and Dr. Nuth at NASA hypothesized that Dr. Louis A. Frank's water balls cannot survive the deep transits through space due to impending cosmic rays, the problem was not solved. Also, cosmic rays from the sun should produce a chemical reaction in the water balls and cause heat to be formed, thus disintegrating the water (disabling their transit through space at the origin) and the heat making the water balls detectable on infrared satellites. Because they were not detected on infrared satellites ever, Dr. Nuth became disturbed at Dr. Frank's water ball (small comet) hypothesis.

Yet when Dr. Frank had sent me pages and diagrams of his data about the water balls (small comets), it seemed very clear that the objects were behaving like water balls impacting the upper atmosphere at a rate of 10-20 million impacts per year. But with that many random and unintelligent impacts, Dr. Nuth wrote to me on February 19, 1999, that:

> As an exercise, I'd suggest that you count the number of objects between the earth and the shuttle (assume an altitude of ~300 miles and that the top of the atmosphere is at ~100 miles), use this to calculate a "space density" for these objects (Dr. Frank's water balls). Multiply this space density by the mass of the objects to figure the influx of material to the surface of the Earth. Or, use this density to figure the time for the shuttle or an average satellite to be struck by one of these objects. Not only is the mass flux much too high to ignore, but no satellite has a chance of surviving days, let alone years if these were actually meteors.

We can see the madness that these two scientists are faced with here. With the mass influx of 10-20 million 40-ton balls of water traveling at 35,000 miles per hour impacting Earth, unless Dr. Frank's water balls were some kind of intelligence or intelligent beings in transit, at a random rate of deposition into the Earth, the shuttle and all of our satellites would have been struck by and be destroyed by these objects. No satellite or the space shuttle has ever been struck by one of these objects. This fact disturbed NASA in regards to Frank's discovery of 10-20 million impending water balls per year. The only logical alternative is that the water balls are actually intelligently directed or maneuvered as spacecraft so that they would not hit our satellites or spacecraft. The only way this could happen would be if the water balls seen by Louis A. Frank were maneuvering themselves around the satellites and the shuttle by means of technology and intelligence, the same way a human astronaut would go around an obstacle.

This evidence would mean that we could clearly hypothesize, with all the evidence pointing to Sirius, and Sirians visiting Earth as amphibians, that these water balls photographed by NASA scientist Dr. Louis A. Frank are Sirians in transit to Earth. Also, that they are still trying to help us by healing the Ozone layer and telling us about Zero-Point energy (stated in previous chapters).

The only answer to the heated debate at NASA about Dr. Louis A Frank's discovery of the water balls ("small comets") is to suggest that the water balls are intelligent life forms or other forms of intelligent craft. As Dr. Nuth at NASA told me in 1995, "In spite of the fact that many people are sure that Frank's explanation for his observations are incorrect, there has been no good alternative explanation proposed yet."

As an answer to the debate at NASA, this is a very powerful statement to show modern scientific data and ancient wisdom matching perfectly with the signature of a race of beings who visited Earth thousands of years ago and that now they have returned. We could also suggest that they have always been in transit between Sirius and Earth as they are our friends and have been for millennia.

When Robert Temple wrote that the Dogon spoke of an "interstellar ship" being encased with "a thin metal shell (hence perfectly round) inflated or manufactured here in the solar system, which is essentially hollow, perhaps even largely empty like a balloon, or containing water at the center, suitably insulated and heated to prevent it from becoming ice," he was inadvertently describing Dr. Louis A. Frank's discovery of the invading water balls mystery without ever having seen his data. He couldn't have seen his data because Frank made his first observations of the water balls in 1985. Temple published his book "The Sirius Mystery" in 1976.

When I wrote Dr. Nuth at NASA in 1994 that the only way I thought water balls could survive in space would be, "How would any object made mostly of H2O (in liquid form) survive in space over any great distances unless it had some kind of phenomenal membrane to protect it from cosmic rays," I was correct. Temple wrote that the

Sirian water balls would have to be "encased with a thin metal shell" probably because he understood the same thing. If they were coated with a thin metallic shell acting as a radiant barrier protecting the water from cosmic rays, they could transit through deep space, but they would still need a form of propulsion of be set inside of giant spacecraft and then let out above the Earth to be intelligently directed down to Earth; thus they would not hit any of our satellites and be so well disguised in water balls.

The Dogon tribe, says Temple, tell of the return of the Sirians as a prophecy:

We should not forget the Dogon say that the Nommos will return, and when they do it will be called "The Day of the Fish." The first indication of their return, say the Dogon, will be that a new star will appear in the sky – the "star of the tenth moon" will have returned. Elements which are at the moment retracted inside this body will re-emerge. Then the Nommos will land on the Earth again in their Ark – the landing craft which makes a lot of noise and emits fire. From this will emerge 'the mythical ancestors" namely the very same personalities who figure in all the myths. This reinforces the notion that they never died and never left the solar system. After their return, this group of Nommos "will rule from the waters." So there will presumably be considerable political implications to their arrival! However, it is most unlikely that they will be hostile to humans, since they have invested so much of their efforts in trying to help this planet develop civilization thousands of years ago that they won't want to see all of their work go to waste. They would be doubtless to be helpful, therefore, but not a little distressed. As aquatic beings, one doesn't have to be a genius to realize that the present state of the world's oceans will greatly upset them, and they might take drastic steps about that. Can you imagine yourself as a Nommo swimming in the sea coming up for air only to have a plastic bottle bump against your nose? And number one on their list would probably be the control of oil spills at sea. Think like a Nommo: what would they want most? Clean seas, of course. They are bound to have advanced technologies for cleaning up the seas very promptly. So they will be very popular with environmentalists and will probably form alliances with the world's "green" parties. Maybe it is the future friends of the Nommos who will be the true "little green men."

In the last intelligent letter I received from the NASA scientist who made the discovery of the water balls, Dr. Louis A. Frank, after he had seen the NASA UFO video, he wrote:

Dear David, I have received your second video and letter dated 2 December 1999. I find the contents of both videos fascinating. There are several objects, which may be small comets (water balls) in the videos. Other phenomenon being recorded in the videos are not easily explained. Several of us have examined the videos many times.

The "other phenomenon being recorded in the videos" that "are not easily explained" are most likely the giant UFOs seen on the STS-75 NASA mission. Could the giant 2-3 mile-wide UFOs in the STS-75, 1996 "Tether Incident" be the Sirian ships or "the new star" in the sky that the African Dogon say contains the Nommos? When we see how perfectly they match with the Chinese Dropa stone discs (which are Sirian in origin say the Dropas), this could actually be so perfect to say "yes" I believe. Could the water balls be coming out of the giant Sirian craft be actual Sirian beings (as amphibians) and be on Earth in our oceans right now? Based on how great the mystery is at NASA into Dr. Louis A. Frank's discovery of water balls that defy logic and science for random natural objects, I believe the only answer to the debate is intelligence.

I believe that both the scientific and historic ancient records point to the very distinct possibility that all of this is happening right under our noses, but we lack the awareness to see what is plain and in our sight. The Sirians have arrived as prophesied. When will they make contact, or has the contact already begun?

Conclusions

I never think of the future - it comes soon enough – Albert Einstein

We have demonstrated three very distinct signatures in the NASA UFO investigation that all point to Sirius. The signatures all stem from the same phenomenon as we have demonstrated.

The first signature pointing to Sirius is the fact that the 1996, NASA STS-75 "Tether Incident" UFOs match perfectly with the ancient Chinese "Dropa Stones." When the discs inscriptions were translated, they told of crashed spacecraft from the star system of Sirius.

The second signature pointing to Sirius comes from comparing Robert Temple's research about what the ancients told of the Sirians: that they are amphibious and would travel to Earth in watery-like space craft. This was synonymous with NASA scientist Dr. Louis A. Frank's discovery of 40-ton water balls the size of small houses entering and impacting with Earth's atmosphere at a rate of 10-20 million per year. The phenomenally high number of these giant water balls made it impossible for them to avoid collisions with satellites and the space shuttle if they could not intelligently maneuver themselves around these obstacles. We deducted that the phenomenon photographed by Dr. Frank was real, as he has proven it, and that the water balls must have maneuvered themselves around the obstacles; thus proving they have intelligence. It was then that we saw a perfect signature match to how the ancient sources tell us that the amphibious Sirians would travel to Earth from Sirius: encased in watery-like space craft.

The third signature pointing to Sirius was the simple fact that the Space shuttle was flying directly over North West Africa, the current home of the African Dogon tribe, who prophesied the return of the Sirian Nommos.

If all of this was just a coincidence, and the real truth was consistent with what Clare Williams and other scientists at NASA were contending, that all of these alleged UFOs were just "floating debris and ice crystals in front of the space shuttle camera lens," then the truth is not as strange as fiction. That possibility disturbs me so much that I do not believe it yet for myself. I do not believe that all of these amazing coincidences have just randomly occurred in this investigation. I believe NASA is really covering up this amazing proof of contact with an extraterrestrial civilization. More importantly, this is contact with the Sirian civilization, the civilization that is the home, say ancient sources, of the creators of human civilization. A fact like this and an incident like this should not be kept from any person alive on this planet. This is why I hope this message is proliferated all over the world.

But of course, like any good researcher, I have to be open to the possibility that this is all just a coincidence. The only way I could get the truth would be to train and go up on the space shuttle with a high-tech video camera capable of seeing into the Near Ultraviolet light spectrum and see for myself, and act as an honorable witness to all of those Americans and world citizens who want to know the answer to the age old question "Are we alone in the universe" and is the hypothesis that NASA has made contact with the Sirian civilization the actual truth?

The Twentieth Century Fox TV special, "UFOs, The Best Evidence Caught On Tape II," produced by Robert Kiviat, aired on Fox TV to over 20 million people on April 27th, 2000. I immediately got flooded with e-mails from NASA scientists who had seen me on the show with their space shuttle footage. They were concerned about public perception for sure, but they also shared a good sense of humor. They were not taking this seriously because they didn't want the public to take it all seriously. The Fox TV special was a sensational news piece showing me talking briefly about the amazing size of the alleged NASA UFOs.

James Oberg, the former NASA mission communications specialist at Houston Mission Control, and current NASA press correspondent at ABC News wrote me on April 27th, after the show, "Congratulations to David Sereda for appearing on FOX's UFO special tonight before a national TV audience."

I decided to write Dr. Joe Nuth at NASA and tell him that I thought the only way to solve this debate would be to put me up on the Space Shuttle with a camera and see for myself and all of those who want me to see what is really going on up there on April 30, 2000, the following letter just after the Fox TV special aired:

Dear Dr. Nuth,

There are too many reasons why I cannot concede that the alleged debris on the STS-75 mission are really debris. I am convinced that there is something going on in space that the agency doesn't want us to know about. The only way I will concede to these objects being debris is if NASA sends me on a space shuttle mission with a working UV camera (I will test it before I go up) so that I can make observations myself and for the UFO community at large. I have over 200 skydives, night jumps and high altitude jumps. I am not afraid to fly on the shuttle for a week and solve this. I am serious. Pass this note onto your buddies at NASA. If I do not see anything up there but junk, I will concede. If NASA will not send me up there, I will attest that NASA has something to hide: that which they do not want the public to see.

I received Dr. Nuth's reply in a few days:

Dear Mr. Sereda,

There are thousands of people who want to become astronauts (including me) but who are precluded by either medical conditions of a very minor nature or by age. You can believe whatever you want, but unless you pass the tests required to become an astronaut, I doubt that you will ever fly on the Shuttle. The alternative would be to get a presidential-level dispensation for your particular purpose, as has occasionally happened in the past for purely political reasons. You are welcome to petition your Congressional Representative or Senators as a start to the process.

In any case, sending you up would not solve the problem for a "true believer" left on the ground. Such a person would simply claim that you, yourself, just became part of the conspiracy and simply "sold out" either for the ride or for some imagined sum of cash. There would be nothing that you could do or say to persuade such a person that you were simply telling the truth. In fact, the harder you tried to convince them of the veracity of your observations, the more convinced they would become that you had indeed sold out - or been brainwashed, or some other nonsense. You really need to think about your claims, beginning with the one that asserts that NASA is trying to cover up a Huge event - contact with another intelligent species - but still sends down totally uncensored TV coverage of shuttle flights on a continuous basis. Or that we are somehow all part of the massive conspiracy - NASA could not keep a secret if its life depended upon it.

Finally, think about the claims you made concerning several mile-wide spacecraft. It is easy to see satellites and shuttles from the ground. Think how easy it would be to spot a formation of mile-wide spacecraft. A large fraction of the planet should have made such sightings by now, yet the only place I've heard that has captured such images are the secret NASA tapes broadcast to anyone who wanted to pick up the signal.

15 years ago I spent a year working at NASA Headquarters in a very junior capacity and was given the job, among others, of answering letters from a variety of individuals writing to the Solar System Exploration Division that no one there wanted to touch. I responded politely to people who claimed that we had never been to the moon - or into space - but that it was all done in a movie studio; to people who were certain that the Earth was hollow and that the entrance to the interior was in Antarctica; to individuals who knew that NASA had already contacted alien races through the SETI program, or who were certain that NASA was covering up the fact that Viking had found actual life on Mars. These people were sincere in their beliefs and I am sure that nothing I could write, no evidence I could send them, would ever convince them to change their minds.

My advisor (Dr. Isadore Adler) told me a story of such an individual. When he worked in the Lunar Receiving Lab during Apollo, a friend brought his father in to see the Moon rocks and tried to impress the father by telling him that the rock he was holding was nearly 4.5 billion years old. The man was a devout Jew and told his son that this was just not possible - the rock could not be much more that 6000 years old. When Izzy tried to help by explaining the radioactive dating method used to determine the age of each lunar sample, the accuracy of the method, etc., the man was undeterred. He believed in the Torah - God had simply used old materials when he constructed the Universe. Even though I admire the man's faith, I do not want to ignore observations or twist reality to make it conform to my own beliefs. Belief can be a very powerful and very dangerous emotion. It can perform miracles and produce suicide bombers. Your beliefs are your own business, not mine.

Jim Oberg has a perfectly reasonable explanation for the shuttle camera observations. You could test the possibility on the ground by getting similar cameras and setting up several test cases to mimic the observations. I will be happy to continue our correspondence in the capacity of someone you might be able to bounce ideas to, on an informal basis, in order to check for obvious flaws. I will not challenge your integrity or intelligence due to your beliefs, but I doubt that I will ever share them.

Sincerely,

Joe Nuth

I really appreciated Dr. Nuth's honesty and his intelligence. I really did. I also appreciated the time he spent with me in this investigation. But even he has not been up there on a mission to see for himself. I wanted to persist with the idea that I should go up in the space shuttle to see for myself and act as a witness to the millions of Americans and world citizens who believe something is going on up there. I wrote him again on May 1, 2000:

Dear Dr. Nuth,

As for the flight physical, I will have no problem. I am very physically fit. I can run uphill for 4 miles non-stop, have made physical examinations for high-altitude skydiving at Edwards AFB, and can handle body fear very well. I don't know about the isolation chamber part of it, but there are windows on the shuttle. They can also throw me outside with my UV sensitive video camera for a while and I will be fine floating 300 miles above our Earth. Who would be a good Senator to deliver supporting signatures for such an endeavor? Thank you for your help. I want you to know that if I do not see anything unusual up there but debris, (and I will check what it looks like out-of-focus) I will concede to the theory that the objects on the STS-75 mission may be debris.

He wrote me back the next day:

Dear Mr. Sereda,

You should always start with your own senators.

Joe Nuth

And that is what I and other people who want to support this initiate would have to do. I would have to get my readers to support me on this. I hope that all of you listen and write to your local senators and ask that I be put on the space shuttle to accomplish this task, to find out what is really going on up there.

After reading Joe Nuth's replies to me, I really think he believes nothing unusual, other than Dr. Louis A. Frank's unsolved mystery is going on up there. Perhaps this really "is" all happening right under NASA's nose, and even they cannot see it. Wouldn't that be amazing, I thought. All this time, the extraterrestrials were visiting us, right under the arrogant noses of the astronauts and the Space Agency, and they didn't even notice.

I again think of the master Jesus' words to St. Thomas some 2000 years ago, from the Nag Hammadi Library, Gospel of Thomas, "Recognize what is in your sight, and that which is hidden from you will become plain to you. For there is nothing hidden which will not become manifest."

Then I received this amazing e-mail letter from James Oberg on May 28, 2000:

Persistent viewers of NASA TV were rewarded Saturday night between 8:59 and 9:04 PM CDT with a five-minute sequence of a brightly flashing object hovering near Atlantis's tail, against the blackness of space beyond. Some flashes of light were downright glaring in brilliance. It seemed to move up and down the edge of the tail. This one's gonna be a keeper — it'll make the next FOX special fer shoor!

I had just appeared Fox Television special called "UFOs, The Best Evidence Caught on Tape II," with sensational clips from the NASA UFO footage on April 27, 2000. The show was broadcast to some 20 million viewers who watched in utter amazement.

On March 12, 2001, I appeared on the Art Bell radio show in a showdown on my findings and investigation with James Oberg to an audience of over 5 million listeners world wide. Never before had NASA participated in such a large public debate on UFOs. It was an intensely furious debate between Oberg and myself. We were arguing over the February, 1996, STS-75 Tether Incident UFOs, the largest UFOs ever captured on film, I measured at 2-3 miles in diameter.

While I was debating with Oberg about why NASA was making observations in higher dimensions of light (in the UV range), and that SETI, looking in the radio spectrum was finding nothing because I hypothesized radio was too low in energy, suddenly the radio show was turned off. It was later found that at the exact same moment, the broadcast satellite was turned off and the internet broadcast was turned off both at the same time. They are not related systems. What happened?

For 18 minutes, technicians at Art Bell's Premiere Radio Network were trying to get the show back on with a ground-based broadcast system. Eighteen minutes of the show was snipped from the airwaves, and mysteriously the satellite turned back on just as the show was finishing. It was all too mysterious as to why the show was turned off.

The next evening, March 13, Art Bell had his technicians go live to reveal that they could not find a mechanical reason for the failure, deduced that solar flares could not have effected the satellite due to its position on the dark side of the Earth, and that the strength of the signal capable of blacking out both the satellite and the internet broadcast would have to be of a magnitude so great, only military installations could be suspect. Was this proof of "Big Brother" intervention imposing National Security to shut down a sensitive broadcast show?

It was the second time in the history of Art Bell's show that a satellite was turned off in the middle of a broadcast. But it was the first time that both the internet and satellite broadcasts were both shut down.

On March 14, 2001, Art Bell received this letter, which he read openly on the air:

The Answer to Who Cut Your Show

Dear Mr. Bell,

This is a letter which has taken me 2 days to gather the courage to write. On one hand I have information as to how, why and whom has cut your show on both occasions. On the other a very well paying job to protect and a family to feed and a friendship to lose. But after contemplating on this matter for said time, I have decided that this country has nothing without freedom, be it press, speech and the like.

Two days ago I spoke with a friend who works in a 3 letter Agency N_ _ . He sounded really tired, and being near noon this was very unlike him. I asked did he have a hot date the night before. He answered "No, I was working late with TEAM "AB." What's that I asked? He replied, "You know that radio show you like so much? And being I only listen to one, which is Art Bell, I said "Yes." He said "Well, last night we had to slap his hand again." I then followed with "Why was that?" He said "AB was opening doors and topics on the air that aren't good for this country at this time, and so we slapped his hand and knocked his butt off the air.

Last time we slapped his hand for having the TRADER LINE (I.E. AREA 51 line). We go through a lot of trouble to have top secret personnel sign secrecy agreements in our country's best interest and AB openly invites them to break law and oaths that they have taken. Bottom line, AB makes trouble for us and we make trouble for him." I then asked "How can you knock him off the air?"

He said "we have control over all media links, and although we used a different method the first time, it's just as easy as opening your garage with the push of a button. It's getting the order that's hard. Making the call when and where, as AB pretty much pushes the boarder every night he is on the air. But last night he was going too far with names and things said in NASA's area were well into the area of National Security. One of the names given as a source for information won't be so willing to speak openly again after today." He then said he had to get off the phone, his wife wanted to use it, end of call.

A couple of things I have deduced from the phone calls with this friend:

This agency has a group of people called Team AB who's job is to listen to your show each night you're on.

A name given on your show the night your show was cut from the air will not be so open with David B. Sereda in the future.

A comment was made in the fashion of we hear everything AB does both On and OFF the air (I.E. bugs).

He said later over a beer after softball that same night, "We got AB from space this time. Next time we will have an EMP truck at his location to even handle AB's Back-Up signal. He said EMP with a very evil grin, "Then he will really learn his lesson.

I have never written a show before, but we need to have freedom in this country without Big Brother's thumb on the button. I may lose a friend over this letter, but I did what I feel is right. God bless

It seemed that this was just a conspiracy theory. But I had to test it again. I decided to write letters to all of my scientists at NASA to see if they really were not going to speak to me. I wrote them all. I never received one answer. It was true. No one at NASA was speaking to me anymore. No one but James Oberg.

James Oberg wrote me on December 11, 2001 to argue about the tether once again. He said I was not presenting all the facts. He still thought it was an apparition caused by the CCD in the video camera. I wrote him the following letter the same day:

Dear Jim,

I did do a video camera test as you suggested and you failed. Once the CCD Video camera is in focus on a distant object such as the tethered satellite 77-100 miles away, then everything is in focus including near-field objects.

I held a set of keys 4 inches in front of the camera while focused on a tree 200 feet away. Both remain in perfect focus. Even Dr. Nuth admitted to the good depth of field of these cameras. This means that if an object 4 inches from the camera is in focus simultaneous to the distant object being in focus, there can be no possible appearances of "Airy Discs" around pieces of junk or debris. So out-of-focus blobs or optical illusions like you are supposing cannot occur.

The video camera I used is certainly not as good as the ones used on the shuttle. Also, the only time I could produce "Airy Discs" in my video camera tests was when I threw the whole camera out of focus. When this happens, everything is a blur and no distinctions can be made about anything. We know from the STS-75 tether incident that Claude Nicollier said, "I'm trying to adjust the focus, but I can't get any better than that."

The camera is too easy to focus. These hi-tech video cameras can be focused on distant objects by a child they are so easy to use. We know he had the camera in focus and that means everything, including near-field objects would also be in focus, so no fuzzy orbs could appear, and certainly could not appear to pass behind the tether 77 miles away.

I even have video from the shuttle where we see a spot on the window in focus while the cam was also in focus on the Earth below, once again demonstrating phenomenal depth of field, as is common with good CCD video cameras. Even in this scene, we can see objects between the near point (the dust on the window) and the far point (the Earth) that appear as our classic disc-shaped objects. With the near field and distant points in focus, nothing in between could be out of focus, as the law of depth of field demonstrates.

David Sereda

He immediately wrote me back retracting his statement saying that the camera had no CCD. He was spinning and retracting statements because he knew he was losing the argument. So I wrote him back te following letter:

Dear James Oberg,

The camera from STS-75 is a Video camera with a good CCD imaging chip. Even you argued that point that it was a CCD camera on our show on Art Bell. You said it was the CCD in the camera producing the apparition. I even know the camera model number from STS-75 and it is a whopper of a camera. This camera is far beyond any other one I have studied. It is better than the CCD camera I used for my own tests by far. NASA took Hasselblad (the best stills camera ever made) to the moon. They only use the very best quality cameras made on their missions. Most of their cameras are retrofitted with better CCDs and other imaging chips to improve their ability to see into alternate spectra of light in the electromagnetic spectrum, which I know well. I have worked professionally with cameras of so many kinds, including super-8 and video, for over 20 years.

Dr. Joseph Nuth, III has confirmed the shuttle video camera's capabilities with me. He also told me about the very good depth of field which I have confirmed in the videos with other UFOs showing similar characteristics. From STS-80, I see a spot on the window of the shuttle in-focus while simultaneously the Earth (some 300 miles below) is simultaneously in-focus. This establishes the camera's phenomenal depth of field. That means nothing in between those two points (the spot on the shuttle window and the Earth below) can be out of focus. This therefore proves that the UFOs are not out of focus Airy Discs and cannot be out of focus. The Unidentified Flying Objects are passing in between the two points of focus and cannot be out of focus objects as some people at NASA contend. Other more intelligent people at NASA , and myself, remain mystified by the phenomena!

David Sereda

James Oberg wrote me back again trying to say that he had made a mistake on the Art Bell show and that the camera had no CCD. He was lying to try and win the argument. Still, with no CCD in the video camera, his theory would lose in all ways. James Oberg was spinning and NASA would now try to change the data and try to win the argument. But they could not win.

I hope he keeps an open mind, as all of us may also try. For some of us, this investigation will suffice to say that the truth has been uncovered. For others, they will have to wait until the Sirians land on the White House lawn and awake the President of the United States and his family to announce, in perfect English, that they have arrived.

Many thanks to Martyn Stubbs, the man who recorded this NASA UFO material, and a man I greatly admire, as he suffers from a brain tumor that may cost him his life. Also, special thanks to Michael Boyle for introducing me to the material. And to all the researchers whose shoulders I stood on to see deeper into this mystery, especially Robert Temple for his work on "The Sirius Mystery." If we read his work, the significance of the possible return of the Sirian Gods and Goddesses to Earth will strike us like lighting.

Terra Entertainment

For a catalog of our products, please contact:

Terra Entertainment
12335 Santa Monica Blvd #336
Los Angeles, CA 90025
(310) 268-1210
www.shopterra.com